TRILOGY

Among Paths to A Christ Mem

Miriam
the
Eden
mas
ory

Truman Capote
Eleanor Perry
Frank Perry

TRILOGY

AN EXPERIMENT IN MULTIMEDIA

introduction by
John M. Culkin, S.J.

The Macmillan Company

Photographs for Miriam *by Lewis Goldman,*
for Among the Paths to Eden *by Martin Harris,*
for A Christmas Memory *by Muky.*

Book designed by Joan Stoliar

Library of Congress Catalog Card Number: 70–90221

First Printing

The Macmillan Company

Collier-Macmillan Canada Ltd., Toronto, Ontario

Printed in the United States of America

for Miss Sook Faulk
in memory of her spirit

contents

Miriam

Among the Paths to Eden

A Christmas Memory

TRILOGY

an experiment in multimedia:
an introduction by John M. Culkin, S.J.

INVOLVES three stories, three people and three media. The short stories
are the work of Truman Capote. The other two people are Frank
and Eleanor Perry, the director-writer team who have given us
David and Lisa, Ladybug, Ladybug, The Swimmer and *Last
Summer*. The three media are print, television and film.

The Perrys first collaborated with Truman Capote in the
television production of *A Christmas Memory*. Eleanor Perry
worked with Capote in the preparation of the script for the one
hour (fifty-two minutes playing time) dramatic program which
was produced and directed by Frank Perry. The critics and the
public universally welcomed it as one of television's finest
hours. Two more short stories—(*Miriam* and *Among the Paths
to Eden*)—were produced for television in the same manner. The
150 minutes of television were then edited to 110 minutes for
distribution as a feature-length film entitled *Truman Capote's
Trilogy*.

This book is a case study of the process by which these
stories found expression in three different media. The idea grew
out of an encounter between the Perrys and some 600 teachers
at the 1967 Washington Film Conference. The audience was
shown the work print of *Trilogy* which Frank Perry still was
editing. Most of them had seen *A Christmas Memory* and *Among
the Paths to Eden* on television. In what someone referred to as
"an intellectual sneak preview" the audience was invited to pass
in a written evaluation of the film and then to discuss the film

with the Perrys. It was a cinematic love-in. Involvement was high because the audience was made part of the directorial decision process. The experience of that day changed both the film and the audience. Frank Perry went back to the editing room and made seven changes in the final version of the feature film. The teachers went back to school with some insight into the filmmaking process, the nature of the media involved and the subtle problems of cross-media translation. My conspiratorial mind envisioned a book which would share this experience and these insights with the rapidly growing breed of film aficionados. The Perrys and Truman Capote generously joined the conspiracy.

A brief note on terminology. These days the walls are down between the various media of communication. Dancers interact with films. Light shows explode with wild combinations of sight, sound and movement. Art and technology are meeting at the growing edge of contemporary experimentation. A new vocabulary has emerged to describe these new phenomena: mixed-media, happenings, multimedia, intermedia, kinetic environment, cross-media, mixed means. Usually these terms are used to define situations in which a variety of media are utilized simultaneously if not synchronously. The term *multimedia* is employed in this book to trace the sequential evolution of a single story through its successive development in several media.

Although we have been cautioned by D. H. Lawrence to trust the tale and not the teller, today's readers and viewers cannot resist the lure of a look behind the scenes. This is especially true of young people who have a special thing going with the movies. They get turned on when the projector gets turned on. Increasingly film is becoming their medium—the one in which they both find and express themselves most directly. They do some thinking both before and after the film. They talk about films—sometimes for days. And they want to know more about films and about filmmaking.

François Truffaut's recent book *Hitchcock* (New York: Simon and Schuster, 1967) and Andrew Sarris' *Interviews with Film Directors* (New York: Bobbs-Merrill, 1968) point a new direction for exploring the filmmaking process. Such face-to-face dialogues with living artists also provide a check on the fanciful

Miriam: *On location in Central Park, Frank Perry directing*

flights occasionally engaged in by some film theoreticians. This study of *Trilogy* works within this new tradition by offering the ingredients and primary sources for a close analysis of a work in process. The original stories and the final script are available for comparison. The commentary by the three principals is designed to fill in the background of their collaboration and to follow the stories through their original production for television and their final form as a film. Although the scripts and anecdotal material are useful in themselves, they will yield their full value only when used in conjunction with the film itself.

In her brilliant essay, *Against Interpretation*, Susan Sontag cautions against the self-conscious and analytical approach to art which substitutes verbalization about experience for the experience itself. "In a culture whose already classical dilemma is the hypertrophy of the intellect at the expense of energy and sensual capability, interpretation is the revenge of the intellect upon art. Even more. It is the revenge of the intellect upon the world."[1] This is a warning desperately needed in the schools where those who live their life above the eyebrows often use the armory of critical apparatus to hold reality at arm's length and to escape the personal involvement and closeness of experience. This same mentality may have occasioned Sam Goldwyn's famous quip, "Don't pay any attention to the critics; don't even ignore them." Frame-by-frame analysis, the search for symbols and over-verbalization are the occupational hazards of a system within which criticism itself has become one of the performing arts. Miss Sontag sounds a more humane note:

> Ours is a culture based on excess, on overproduction; the result is a steady loss of sharpness in our sensory experience. All the conditions of modern life—its material plenitude, its sheer crowdedness—conjoin to dull our sensory faculties. . . . What is important now is to recover our senses. We must learn to *see* more, to *hear* more, to *feel* more.[2]

Most of us who are shouting for some balanced program of media study within the schools share film critic Pauline Kael's caustic reminder that "we should not underestimate the power

[1] Reference notes are on page 15.

of education to kill anything." The clinical and aseptic analysis of literature has ruined books for enough students to make us wary of those who might repeat the atrocity on friendly media like film and television. When in doubt quote Alfred North Whitehead. The sonorous cadence of his name, his wide range of competence and the fact that few people have read him conspire to make him an ideal authority for almost any controversy. In *The Aims of Education*[3] he traces a three-stage rhythm of education which he feels should apply in any learning situation: one, the stage of *romance* in which the intrinsic interest, excitement and wonder of the experience should prevail; two, the stage of *precision* within which the half-glimpsed patterns and causes of that interest are explored and analyzed; and three, the stage of *generalization* which combines these two qualities of intuition and analysis into a harmonious synthesis. That is the spirit of this inquiry into *Trilogy*. It is for the generalist who would like to know what these media are all about without needing to know all about them.

The study of popular media like film and television is gaining ground in American education. What five years ago was looked upon as an educational threat or luxury is now an integral part of the curriculum in hundreds of colleges and high schools. The brief for some kind of media study within the schools normally follows one of two lines of argument: (1) make the media seem so respectable that the schools have to recognize them as worthy of inclusion within the curriculum; or (2) make their impact seem so lethal that the schools feel forced to deal with them as a tactic of survival. Before focusing on *Trilogy* it might be instructive to pull the cameras back for a long shot of the cultural context within which such media analysis is operating.

As Adam once confided to Eve: "We are living in a period of transition." Within the brief span of sixty years we have moved from a speech- and print-dominated culture into a total information and multimedia culture. One does not have to be a card-carrying McLuhanite to acknowledge the pervasive presence of media and messages of all kinds. The television statistics alone are staggering. By the time a student graduates from high school today he has watched more than fifteen thousand hours of television and been in the classroom for less than eleven thousand hours. This communications environment belongs to this century. Many have reacted to it, few have reflected about it, and fewer still have done anything about it. Intelligent living within such a culture calls for some understanding of these media.

Marshall McLuhan, who has achieved brand-name identification with the new media, sets forth a very humane and constructive approach in his introduction to *Explorations in Communications*:

> At the moment, it is important that we understand cause and process. The aim is to develop an awareness about print and the newer technologies of communication so that we can orchestrate them, minimize their mutual frustrations and clashes, and get the best out of each in the educational process. The present conflict leads to elimination of the motive to learn and to diminution of interest in all previous achievement. It leads to loss of the sense of relevance. Without an understanding of media grammars, we cannot hope to achieve a contemporary awareness of the world in which we live. . . . If these "mass media" should serve only to weaken or corrupt previously achieved levels of verbal and pictorial culture, it won't be because there's anything inherently wrong with them. It will be because we've failed to master them as new languages in time to assimilate them to our total cultural heritage.[4]

This positive thrust toward understanding moves beyond any "fallout-shelter" approach to the media and encourages research into the form, structure and process proper to each medium.

The neutral word "medium" has the advantage of being inclusive and of avoiding the tedious discussions about whether or not certain media qualify as art forms. They all qualify as facts within our experience and that would seem to be sufficient reason to examine them. The rationale for this kind of media analysis has been cogently formulated by Edmund Carpenter:

> English is a mass medium. All languages are mass media. The new mass media—film, radio, TV—are new languages, their grammars as yet unknown. Each codifies reality dif-

ferently; each conceals a unique metaphysics. Linguists tell us that it's possible to say anything in any language if you use enough words or images, but there's rarely time; the natural course is for a culture to exploit its media biases.[5]

A sensitivity to the characteristics of each medium can lead to a greater insight into all media and to the relationships among media. The concept of an all-media literacy is far from an attack on or a minimizing of the values of the spoken and written word. It is, however, an acknowledgment of the fact that the introduction of new media in a culture must of necessity change the role of the older media. The printed word will not be best served by those who ignore what is currently happening and who hope that the new media will silently fade away. The new humanities and the new liberal arts must be ecumenical enough to include all media regardless of the conditions of their birth and past history.

Walt Whitman said: "To have great poets, there must be a great audience." Great audiences for any art form are not born; they are made. They are created by an exposure to and an analysis of excellence within the medium. Some people are distracted because film and television are "mere entertainment" (as though that were a bad thing in itself). The same tag once kept Elizabethan drama, the novel and vernacular literature out of the schools. Others stress the number of worthless or tasteless films and television programs. The piffle index, however, is high for any medium, and the percentage of poor films and television is probably about the same as the percentage of poor work in print, paint and other media. The best within the new media deserve the same attention to context and style that we accord to the traditional arts.

Transitions are seldom simple or graceful. Complex issues tend to be reduced to simplistic either-or questions as the shouting gets louder. The studies of Walter Ong have traced the sharp conflicts attending the introduction of contemporary literature into the schools less than seventy-five years ago. Film and television are swimming against the same cultural currents today. It would be lovely to bypass the tedious and predictable interplay between the zealots from both the print and electronic factions and to arrive at an early synthesis which incorporates the best of both worlds. Ong is even more emphatic about the necessary relationship between the two cultures: "Any kind of genuine sensitivity to literature of any age or culture has become thoroughly impossible unless a person has grown seriously— not phrenetically—reflective about contemporary communications media."[6]

This process can be greatly facilitated through the aid of mediators or brokers who understand, respect and work within both traditions. Truman Capote is such an artist. His work gracefully bridges several worlds. It is not just that his writings have supplied the raw material for adaptation for film or television. He has written directly for the new media and has worked closely with those producing his work.

He wrote for the stage in adapting two of his short stories: *The Grass Harp* into a memorable comic-drama and *House of Flowers* into a Broadway musical. *The Grass Harp* has been further adapted by Kenward Elmslie and Claibe Richardson into a Broadway musical. Capote wrote the original screenplay for *Beat the Devil* as it was being shot (each day the actors— Humphrey Bogart, Gina Lollobrigida, Peter Lorre—awaited the new pages of the script, and none but Capote knew how the story would end). He adapted Henry James' *The Turn of the Screw* into the motion picture called *The Innocents*. His penchant to experiment with the forms of communication led him to treat nonfiction as a separate art form at least as powerful as fiction with the scrupulously objective "nonfiction novel" *In Cold Blood*. He completed in 1968, with Leland Hayward as producer, the television documentary *Death Row, U.S.A.*

A Christmas Memory has had as varied a media existence as any work of our time. It was first published in a magazine, later appeared in the same volume as the short novel *Breakfast at Tiffany's,* is included in the Modern Library edition of *Selected Writings of Truman Capote,* and has been published by itself for two Christmas seasons at this writing in a slim gift volume. It has been performed on stage at the Edinburgh Festival. Capote has recorded a reading of the work which has been broadcast several times on radio. The television version was first broadcast in 1967, and promises to be a Christmas perennial on

Among the Paths to Eden: *Eleanor Perry, Martin Balsam, Maureen Stapleton, Truman Capote, Frank Perry*

television. With very minor excisions it was incorporated into *Trilogy* which entered theatrical release in late 1969 and was made available in 16 millimeter shortly thereafter. It will enjoy a long life in all of its forms.

Gerald O'Grady, whose studies of Arthur Miller explore much of this same ground, has coined the phrase "multimedia writer" (in an unpublished manuscript) to describe the writer who has been conditioned by and has confronted the media of our century. He suggests that the study of such writers will demand new knowledge and skills of the scholars who attempt to assess the cultural influence of a work reaching its audience in a multiplicity of forms. Miller's own awareness of the mutual borrowings from various media is shown in his own commentary on *The Misfits*:

> A glance at *The Misfits* will show that it is written in an unfamiliar form, neither novel, play, nor screenplay. A word of explanation is perhaps in order.
>
> It is a story conceived as a film, and every word is there for the purpose of telling the camera what to see and the actors what they are to say. However, it is the kind of tale which the telegraphic, diagrammatic manner of screenplay writing cannot convey because its sense depends as much on the nuances of character and place as on the plot. It therefore became necessary to do more than merely indicate what happens and to create through words the emotions which the finished film should possess. It was as though a picture were already in being, and the writer were recreating its full effects through language, so that as a result of a purely functional attempt to make a vision of a film clear to others, a film which existed as yet only in the writer's mind, there was gradually suggested a form of fiction itself, a mixed form if you will, but one which it seems to me has vigorous possibilities for reflecting contemporary existence. Movies, the most widespread form of art on earth, have willy-nilly created a particular way of seeing life, and their swift transitions, their sudden bringing together of disparate images, their effect of documentation inevitable in photography, their economy of storytelling, and their concentration on mute action have infiltrated the novel and play writing—especially the latter

—without being confessed to or, at times, being consciously realized at all. *The Misfits* avowedly uses the perspectives of the film in order to create a fiction which might have the peculiar immediacy of image and the reflective possibilities of the written word.[7]

On a more mundane level most novelists today are not unaware of the pot of movie gold waiting on the other side of a successful novel. Within recent years producer Joseph E. Levine paid a fee for the film rights to a novel which had not as yet been written.

The short story offers a rich mine of material for film-makers. Unfortunately its length militates against its chances of being financed for theatrical distribution. The stories are usually too slight to be expanded to feature-length films and at present there is no theatrical market for thirty- or forty-minute films. The anthology film, consisting of several short films, has had uneven commercial success in the past. Some of the more notable examples have been *O. Henry's Full House, Quartet, Boccaccio 70, Gold of Naples, Yesterday, Today and Tomorrow, Dead of Night, If I Had a Million, The Seven Deadly Sins* and *Love at Twenty*. Two of the world's great directors, Ingmar Bergman and Federico Fellini, recently announced that they would collaborate on a two-part film exploring the theme of love.

There are some indications that shorter narrative films may find a meaningful place in the shifting media world. Many feature films today seem to take too long to tell their story. The perceptions of the audience have been speeded up by the rapid cutting and telescoping of television commercials. Audiences just catch on faster these days. The National Film Board of Canada has produced two superb narrative films, *Phoebe* and *No Reason To Stay,* which say it all in less than thirty minutes. *The War Game* and *Warrendale* have won wide critical approval but failed in the theaters because they were less than an hour long. I believe, however, there will be a growing market both in the theaters and within the schools for film programs including a variety of shorter films. Some of this kind of booking is already happening now on a happenstance basis. As the audience for such programs emerges, it should be possible to develop a viable method for financing these shorter films. These new audiences might also encourage the television producers to make their materials accessible after they have appeared on television. Perhaps *Trilogy* can test the validity of this concept.

"A translator is a traitor," runs an old adage. This sums up the attitude of those who feel that something is inevitably lost in the transition from one language to another or from one medium to another. This is frequently but not necessarily true. Many films based on books have been unfairly criticized by those whose sole standard is fidelity and who are unaware that change is unavoidable and often desirable in order to conform to the idiom of the new medium. Actually films adapted from fiction have ranged from point-for-point fidelity to the original to films which shared little more with the original than the title which was purchased for its ready-made publicity and pre-conditioned audience.

A famous cartoon depicts two goats lunching on celluloid outside a film studio. The caption reads: "I liked the book much better." Frequently, people prefer the version of a story which they have first experienced. If the film or television viewer has already read the story, he will be comparing the director's interpretation with his own. If one reads a book after having seen the filmed version, the film's images often supply for personal imagination.

There are, however, no rigid ground rules for such adaptation. If a director is working with a property which he respects, his task is to maintain the tone, texture, feel and intent of the original. He must look for the right blend of medium and message so that he achieves through the syntax of image and sound what the writer accomplished with words. And, if in the process, he manages to please the original author, he is twice blessed.

The artist–audience relationship is different for each of the media. Conditions of production, distribution, economics, audience, consumption, and a host of other variables preclude any univocal concept of the artist and his public. Unfortunately our cultural imagination comes equipped with a ready-made image of the traditional artist as one who works alone, in poverty, with paper or paint to produce poems, paintings, and symphonies. The image doesn't work very well any more even for the writers, painters, and composers, and it has nothing at all to do with the craftsmen within film and television who have to work in collaboration with teams of associates, with large budgets, and with frequent forays into the marketplace to deal with bankers. The great American movie can't be produced on the backs of old envelopes.

A painter has to please one patron to sell his work. A novelist can hit the bestseller list with fifteen to twenty thousand well-distributed copies. A playwright needs about one hundred thousand tickets sold on Broadway. A million dollar movie needs more than two and a half million patrons. Prime-time television needs more than twenty million steady viewers. We've come a long way from the one-to-one relationship between De Medici and Michaelangelo. The public has become the patron and, distasteful as this may be to many elitists, this reliance on numbers is a fact of the commercial media. Film and television live not by aesthetics alone. They are what someone has called "a shotgun marriage of commerce and culture."

Television imposes artificial time imperatives on the writer and director. The material must be tailored to fit the Procrustean format of the thirty-minute module and its multiples. Each of the three stories in *Trilogy* was produced for a one hour program slot. Ten minutes of each hour were used by the sponsor "to move the merch," as they say. Fifty minutes proved to be a comfortable length for *A Christmas Memory* but, in my judgment, it put a strain on the fragile and tightly confined relationship described in *Among the Paths to Eden*. The latter story is at its right dramatic length in the final edited version of twenty-five minutes. *Miriam* was trimmed by fifteen minutes, but *A Christmas Memory* has been left almost completely intact for *Trilogy*. In many other countries, like England, Italy and Japan, the clock is more tolerant of dramatic necessity. A program is allowed to run until it has told its story.

The television schedule also makes time demands on the audience. As a one-time only, see-it-now-or-never medium, it doesn't leave its audience any options. Either you are there to catch it at the appointed hour or it whizzes by in the night into the limbo of yesterday's programming. This doesn't hold for books which are the most accessible of the media. And it is less true for films which have a theatrical run of some duration and then eventually find their way into 16-millimeter format and on to "Some-night-or-other at the Movies." New home recording devices will perhaps help TV to break this time barrier in the near future.

Each of the media is also experienced by its consumer under a great variety of circumstances. Print is a private medium, normally experienced alone, and at a pace which is completely under the control of the consumer. Film is usually a public or social medium, experienced in a crowd, in a specially designed environment, and at a non-stop pace predetermined by the director. Television is lots of things to lots of people. The average set is watched by 2.7 viewers under a wide range of viewing conditions, at the director's pace and with the sponsor's interruptions. Film and television also invite comparison on elements such as the size of the image, the quality of the reproduction, and color. *A Christmas Memory*, for instance, does something different to its audience as a black-and-white television show, a color TV show, and a big screen color motion picture.

The final film version of *Trilogy* begins with *Miriam*, follows with *Among the Paths to Eden* and closes with *A Christmas Memory*. When the individual stories are linked together and seen in succession, they pick up resonances from each other; they take on fuller meanings because of this juxtaposition. Eisenstein has commented on this phenomenon of editing in his theories of montage.[8] As Capote points out, the three stories share the common theme of human loneliness. In fact, "The Heart Is a Lonely Hunter" would have been an ideal title, if it had not been pre-empted by Carson McCullers. There is also an internal and successive shading of the degree of loneliness and alienation in each of the stories. Miriam is almost completely cut off as a person; Mary O'Meaghan has some hope and is still in competition; in *A Christmas Memory* there is love.

Trilogy was one of the two American films selected in competition for the 1968 Cannes Film Festival. The other film was *Petulia* whose director, Richard Lester, previously had made the Beatles' films. *Trilogy* and *Petulia* offer a nice contrast in film styles: each is very different, yet each is right for communicating the mood and pace of its own material. Lester used a quick-cutting, non-linear, zooming style to capture the hectic and mercurial ways of the San Francisco mod atmosphere. It worked. Frank Perry approached his three stories with a thoughtful and gentle film style suited to the intimacy of the relationship being explored. Perry works in close with the camera using the human face as his most dramatic landscape. It is his personal film style and it lent itself admirably to his first venture into television. The small screen encourages such close-ups. It affords a special kind of intimacy and immediacy for small stories like those first produced in television's so-called "Golden Age" by writers like Paddy Chayefsky, Rod Serling and Reginald Rose.

A New York cab driver expounded his personal theory of the universe, took a short breath and said: "That is my opinion and it is very true." Ultimately every man is his own favorite film critic. By definition we are all the expert on what we like best. The real experience of *Trilogy* is in the reading of the stories and in the seeing of the film. Hopefully this stage of romance and enjoyment will be enhanced by the more precise and personal insights provided by *Trilogy's* three authors.

[1] Susan Sontag, *Against Interpretation*. New York: Dell, 1961, p. 13.
[2] Sontag, p. 14.
[3] Alfred North Whitehead, *The Aims of Education*. New York: Macmillan, 1959.
[4] Edmund Carpenter and Marshall McLuhan (eds.), Introduction to *Explorations in Communications*. Boston: Beacon, 1960.
[5] Carpenter and McLuhan, p. 162.
[6] Walter Ong, *The Barbarian Within*. New York: Macmillan, 1962, p. 229.
[7] Arthur Miller, Introduction to *The Misfits*. New York: Viking, 1961.
[8] Sergei Eisenstein, *Film Form and Film Sense*. Translated by Jay Leyda. New York: Meridian, 1960.

TRILOGY

a reminiscence by Truman Capote

ONE AUTUMN MORNING three years ago a young director named Frank Perry telephoned me and said he wanted to make an hour-length television film from my autobiographical short story, *A Christmas Memory*. I had never met Mr. Perry, or his wife and professional partner, Eleanor; but I knew them by reputation, and understood them to be gifted, conscientious artists.

In the past, a number of people had wanted to dramatize this story in one form or another, but I had always felt reluctant about it, for the story has a deep personal meaning to me. Also, I had always thought that, if photographed, it should be a silent film of flowing images explained by music and narration. No one altogether agreed with that, and they were quite correct; and no one agreed that I myself should be the narrator—something I insisted on, not out of vanity, but because it was my story, in every sense, and I wasn't going to allow any "distinguished baritone" to tell it.

Mr. Perry, dark and jovial as a gypsy porpoise, conceded that point, even seemed enthusiastic; and as I liked all his other ideas, the casting, the notion of filming it on location in my childhood country, rural Alabama, we set to work and eventually combined ourselves, Frank, Eleanor and I, into a truly collaborative trio.

To say that I was satisfied with the filmed *A Christmas Memory* is a considerable understatement. Frank's directorial understanding, Eleanor's delicate suremindedness with the script, and the fantastic (using this word at its subtlest) perceptivity of Geraldine Page's playing, resulted in an extraordinarily accurate recreation of the original story. And let me say, friends: this is not simple to do—to translate from one media to another (and another, and another) the mood and intent of the matrix work.

Which is what the present volume is about: the problem of reinterpreting the same material in differing forms and circulating them by the various available routes: magazines, books, recordings, television specials, feature films. Though created years apart, each of the stories that comprise *Trilogy* underwent these transformations. *Miriam* was written when I was seventeen and was among my first published stories; *A Christmas Memory* appeared in 1956—I wrote the whole story during one hot January night in Hong Kong, a landscape and a mood greatly removed from Alabama's remembered frost and silence. *Among the Paths to Eden* was the last short story I wrote before climbing into the ring for my five-year battle with *In Cold Blood*.

Why, among my stories, did we select these particular three? Because, despite the dissimilarities of setting—Manhattan, a Queens cemetery, a farm in Alabama—they have a subject in common: loneliness. Loneliness; love; lack of love. It is as though one held a multi-tinted lozenge to the light, turned it this way

and that catching separate colors in the same prism. Also, each of these stories offered, in their central roles, special opportunities for three actresses of important excellence—our three ladies: Geraldine Page, Maureen Stapleton and Mildred Natwick. Perhaps *Trilogy's* most interesting element is the quality of the performances: it seems to me a brief anthology of the best in American acting styles.

In listing the different transformations through which these tales have traveled, I notice that I failed to mention the one that in some ways I find the most gratifying: the public reading. The appurtenances of these readings, usually presented in university auditoriums, have a touch of the *guignol*—the beforehand faculty dinner, the reception afterward. *But*—once the lights have darkened, and the voice takes charge, silencing the audience, weaving through and molding them into emotional shapes, then a writer can feel the most intense artistic communication, for he has become a storyteller in the oldest and purest form: a figure by the firelight driving the cold out of the hearts, the sound of wind and thoughts of disaster from the heads of his listeners.

Now that *Trilogy* is completed, I look forward to collaborating with the Perrys on another trio of short films. Actually, we have already finished one: *The Thanksgiving Visitor*. In other words—*à bientôt*.

"Our three ladies"
(left to right)
Maureen Stapleton,
Mildred Natwick,
Geraldine Page

TRILOGY

a reminiscence by Frank Perry

NINE YEARS AGO when I first read *A Christmas Memory,* I had not directed so much as a home movie. Yet I knew that I must turn this exquisite story into a film.

I'd put in a solid fourteen years preparing for what I believed to be my vocation—Broadway director.

Beginning as a fifteen-year-old car park attendant at the Westport Playhouse, graduating to full-fledged apprentice, studying "theater arts" in college, going on to more summers in stock, working variously as assistant stage manager, actor, electrician, lighting designer, stage manager, assistant producer, director, producer, managing director, all in the bush leagues. Then New York. Direction classes with Lee Strasberg, stage managing on Broadway, associate producer for the Theatre Guild, director/ observer at the Actors Studio. Studying, fighting, reading, thinking: theater, theater, theater!

But, gradually, a growing doubt. Was something *wrong* with theater? Wasn't the excitement for me, personally, diminishing? Where were the plays? The playwrights? Broadway seemed to be suffocating in the heavy cloak of its own establishment, and after jocular decades of referring to itself as the "fabulous invalid," was sicker than it knew.

Then 1960: *Hiroshima Mon Amour, Four Hundred Blows*. Film after brilliant film from Europe, made by artists for adults. Films with things to say and a dynamic new way to say them. My disenchantment with the theater was complete. Eleanor Perry, a talented Broadway playwright and recently my wife, agreed. As excited as I was by what was coming to us from France and Italy, she wanted to write movies as much as I wanted to make them.

And so, rather like country mice setting out to see the queen, we set out to make a film.

We began to read as a pair possessed—books on theory of film, techniques of film, directing, cutting, screenwriting and, above all, *properties*. Fiction, nonfiction, stories, articles, anything we thought we would want to tell on film.

After months of reading, the first thing which really worked for me—which I could *see* as film—was the Capote story. I knew it must be filmed, but worried about the length—was it full enough for a feature film? Eleanor, on the contrary, pointed out many possible departure points for expansion, which she records later in this book.

I telephoned Capote's agent, Audrey Wood, the next morning to inquire about the motion picture rights to *A Christmas Memory*. She listened with her customary courtesy, told me there had been many inquiries over the years and that the author had consistently refused to part with the rights as the story was quite "special" to him—but she'd tell him about my call and, in that monstrous phrase so popular in our business, "get back to me." She called in about a week to say that "at this time" there was no interest on the part of the author. File and forget.

A month later I read a fifty-five-page fictionalized case history about two schizophrenic teenagers named David and Lisa, published by the medical department of The Macmillan Company. Once again, I turned to Eleanor and said, "Here it is, but, damn, it's too short—not enough material for a feature film." Once again she pointed out exactly how this simple tale could be expanded into a full-length motion picture.

If lives may be said to have watersheds, I suppose *David*

and Lisa was ours. Certainly it welded us into a team, taught us the pleasures and problems of marital and professional collaboration, and proved to be of measurable door-opening value on our next approach to Miss Wood about *A Christmas Memory,* four years later.

I'd received a call from David Sontag, who had been appointed producer of a new series of one hour TV specials intended to "raise the cultural level" of the medium. The name was *ABC Stage '67* and did we have anything we'd like to do for it?

A Christmas Memory came tumbling back into mind—but could we get the rights? Again the call to Audrey Wood, this time requesting a meeting with Capote to discuss how we saw the story as film.

Word came back immediately: come on over.

We met Truman for the first time in November, 1965, and were instantly captivated. We talked about what *A Christmas Memory* meant to us, its tender lyricism, how it should be done visually, that it must be shot on location in rural Alabama —and, as it was patently autobiographical, that it should be narrated by Truman himself. We three seemed to expand and spark from one another until we were in total agreement about the approach to the story as film.

When told of our meeting, series-chief Sontag was in full accord. However, he had already received a good deal of resistance from the powers at ABC who found the story "slight and sentimental," "lacking in plot," with "no suspense," and "perhaps not quite up to the high dramatic standards we're projecting for *Stage 67.*" Further, Sontag predicted that when they heard we wanted to shoot on location in Alabama, use Geraldine Page as the lead, and have Capote narrate—he really was most dubious about getting a go ahead. However, since he believed in the project, he'd try.

Anticipating this kind of resistance from the network, we had already agreed with Truman that we would not compromise our approach. If we were turned down, we'd take the project to the other networks. If unable to make a deal at any of them, we would then undertake to raise the money ourselves and expand the material into a feature film.

Reluctantly, ABC agreed to go forward, providing we guaranteed completion of the project. That meant we were to be given a certain amount of money for which we must deliver a one hour color film, regardless of how much it cost us. I had already figured that to do the film the way we wished would cost a minimum of $25,000 more than their top offer. This was without paying Eleanor, Truman or myself a cent for what, in Truman's case, was one of his most valuable properties; and in my case, would amount to a good solid six to eight months work. Further, if the production went over budget—and what film doesn't?—we were responsible for the full amount of that overage, a figure which could amount to another hundred thousand dollars or more.

What kind of sense did it make for us to accept this financial risk? I exposed our purpose as inconspicuously as possible in an early meeting with the network. "By the way, we'd like to retain the theatrical rights to this program—world-wide." "*Theatrical* rights?" I nodded quietly. "But those rights won't be worth a cent after it's been on *television!* And only fifty minutes long! The rights you're asking for are meaningless!"

"Okay. So let us have them."

And they did.

With that I felt we had a remote chance, financially.

By now it was early January and time was a problem. We had to have the sere winter landscape in Alabama to create the visual atmosphere. As spring comes early that far south, I committed us to the latest possible start date, February 24th. However, Geraldine Page, who was as excited as we were about the project, was in a Broadway-bound play, which didn't open until the tenth of February. We had heard that the play was not good —and would probably not run. But we couldn't be sure, nor could we help worrying that even with mediocre notices they might eke a run of several weeks. So, we sweated out the opening; and I found myself having the unpleasant experience of rooting in the negative for a play with a friend in the cast for the first (and I hope the last) time.

For A Christmas Memory: *a house with the quality and atmosphere of the one Capote lived in as a boy*

Meanwhile, with cheerful confidence, I put together the production staff and crew, outlined needed script revisions with Eleanor, and with production designer Gene Callahan, left for our first location scouting trip in Alabama.

If possible, I wanted to shoot where the story had taken place, in the actual house in which Truman had lived as a boy. But he felt Monroeville had probably lost the rural quality it had during the Depression. Further, his relatives' house had burned down in the late thirties. Still, he suggested we go there because some of the surrounding towns—Burnt Corn, for example—might still have the right quality. More importantly, he gave us an introduction to an old friend who knew Alabama intimately. The gifted, delightful Nell Harper Lee, author of *To Kill A Mockingbird,* had grown up in the house next door to Capote, and was the perfect consultant on the atmosphere of the early thirties in southern Alabama. We spent a fascinating day with Miss Lee, who showed us the charms of Burnt Corn and the surrounding country. Truman's suspicions were confirmed at once. There was nothing within miles of Monroeville that had the quality we sought. Harper Lee suggested the farmlands just south of Montgomery, and gave us, along with her blessing, a number of priceless recollections about the quality and atmosphere of Truman's house, the bootlegger's cafe that was the model for HaHa Jones, the road on which the "six o'clock bus from Mobile" came through town, and other invaluable notes, impressions and suggestions.

I knew our film must be a tone poem—a lyrical evocation of an innocent time, sweetly recalled, a delicate memory of childhood. As such, the physical production must strive for absolute verisimilitude and poetic beauty. Clearly then, one of the key jobs on the picture was that of production designer. I had the fine fortune to engage an old and dear friend, Gene Callahan, a tall acerbic gentleman with an imposing auburn beard, twice an Oscar winner—for his production design of *The Hustler* and *America, America.* Callahan, now for the first time, was called upon to recreate something that was truly his milieu—the rural South in which he had grown up.

A Christmas Memory: *the preliminary property list included over a thousand objects to evoke the atmosphere of that household*

Callahan's preliminary property list—made after he had read the first draft script, was fifteen pages of single spaced items —totaling over a thousand things and objects which would help evoke the atmosphere of this household. For want of a better phrase, I would term this a "method" prop list: like a superb actor he put himself into the characters and felt the sort of life they would have, the objects that would surround them, the choices they would make as people, housekeepers, toy builders, food buyers. For the kitchen alone, he listed several hundred items which included the following:

Gold Dust Twins soap powder
clear beer bottles for vinegar syrup and (with cork stoppers) for bleach
large pickle crock with gauze over top
large bowl (ocher) filled with eggs
old silver spoon worn flat on end for mixing cakes
two fruit crates lined with old newspapers used for vegetable storage
armoire to be painted (remove panels in doors to be replaced with screening)
Bissel sweeper
cracked soup bowl and chipped agate pan for food and water for Queenie

(See pages 273-276 for the complete list.) This was precisely the sort of attention to detail which all of us knew the production must have.

Following Harper Lee's advice, Callahan and I drove north to Montgomery, where after days of scouting, in the tiny farming community of Snoudown we found precisely the house we wanted for our film.

Back to New York for additional casting: I had to find the boy to play Buddy, a Haha Jones and others. I showed Polaroids of the selected locations to Truman. He thoroughly approved.

However, trouble at ABC. They were reluctant to go ahead, and refused to unless we agreed on a substitute for the lead in case Geraldine Page's play ran. The list they proposed was unacceptable to us. Without such a concession, the network refused to be responsible for the fifty or sixty thousand dollars which we had already spent. To further our difficulties, our friend Sontag, who was responsible for our being involved in *Stage 67*, had been "let go" because it was felt his judgment was "not sufficiently mature." The inference was made that his biggest potential disaster was *A Christmas Memory*. However, the network was prepared to honor its obligation despite the distressing lack of sex, dramatic values, and inherent "TV suitability."

Amid reports from Callahan in Alabama that he was finding "just the things" we needed there—together with the help of a gracious and lovely local lady, Eugenia Tuttle, who became a mainstay of our unit—work continued on assembling the fifty-man crew and cast that would go with us to Alabama. To get the people we wanted, I was forced to make commitments to a number of high-salaried individuals on a "play or pay" basis, i.e., they must be paid for the full shooting time, whether or not we made the picture. All this was done, of necessity, a full week before Geraldine's play opened, so our three-sided personal exposure was increased still more.

Finally, the play did open, was a disaster, and closed ten days later, on Saturday night, the nineteenth of February. The next morning Gerry got on the plane for Montgomery, arriving Sunday night for one day's rehearsal Monday and shooting Tuesday, the twenty-second. As it was, we did the exteriors first and held our breath since buds were full, ripe and about to burst. In fact, in one or two scenes the pale green signs of spring dot the bare branches of our December landscape.

In short, we cut it pretty close.

Shooting was a joy. After the sweat, uncertainty, anxiety, fights with the money people, what is generally regarded as the toughest part—production—was a holiday.

Page was incredible. She refused make up. The characterization came from the inside. After a not particularly emotional scene on the first afternoon of shooting, she seemed close to tears. I tried to find what had moved her. She looked up at me and said, "It's because I'm happy, can't you see? Because I love you and this story and because this is going to be my first good movie!" Warm words from a woman who had been nominated for an Oscar three times!

But, all of us were aware from the first day that we were involved in something special. All our crew had worked frequently on big budget Hollywood and New York feature films—at substantially larger salaries than they were getting on this job. To a man, they gave more effort and attention to our film because we all really cared. I have never worked with a unit which would not respond this way—provided the work was worthy, the individuals treated with respect and brought into a meaningful involvement with the aesthetic and technical problems of the job at hand.

We were scheduled and budgeted for twelve days' shooting: as anticipated, we went over two days for a total of fourteen. On the eighth of March we arrived in New York thoroughly exhausted. I took one day off and plunged into the cutting. There was pressure to work night and day in the editing room, as I wanted to get as far along as possible before putting it aside for necessary work on other projects. I knew I must at least get to a rough cut state to show to Truman before summer. So after two months of around-the-clock editing, I arranged the first screening for an audience of three. Although Truman had recorded his narration for the film weeks earlier, he had not seen a single foot of film. I had no objectivity left. I wasn't sure of anything about the film. Suddenly it seemed presumptuous to be showing a man an episode of his own childhood.

During the screening, Truman sat immobile in front and to the right of us—and while Eleanor watched the film, I watched the back of his head for a clue to his reaction. At last, when the film was over, concealing a small sniffle, he blew his nose, and turned to thank us, his eyes filled. His satisfaction was apparently total, his praise overwhelmingly generous, as it has been ever since.

That screening took place in spring, 1966. That summer I

Frank Perry with Geraldine Page

shot a feature film, *The Swimmer,* which delayed completion of *A Christmas Memory* until late fall. When Truman saw the completed film of his story, he expressed his pleasure and suggested we might think about doing other things of his together.

Later, carrying our thoroughly thumbed copy of the Modern Library collected Capote, we arrived at Truman's house in the Hamptons to spend the weekend. That Saturday night Truman proposed that we do two more stories, to be combined eventually with *A Christmas Memory* into a feature motion picture. After intensive discussion, we agreed that *Miriam* and *Among the Paths to Eden* were those stories. All of us concurred that these studies of the essential loneliness of the human condition had a strong thematic interrelationship and could work symbiotically to form a meaningful whole.

Once again we turned to casting. Truman, with his perceptive grasp of this difficult, underrated facet of filmmaking, immediately proposed Mildred Natwick for *Miriam.* We discussed many people for *Eden* that night as well, agreeing that the ideal cast would be Maureen Stapleton and Martin Balsam.

Thus, a month before the telecast of *A Christmas Memory,* the full plan for *Trilogy* was formed and agreed upon. Needless to remark, if *Christmas* had not been a success on first showing, we could certainly forget our plans for *Trilogy.* Such a possibility, I suspect, did not even remotely occur to Truman.

The telecast was a success, the notices from around the country were without a single exception superb, and the program went on to win eighteen major awards including the prestigious Peabody as best television show of the year, the International Television Critics prize and Emmys for Geraldine, Truman and Eleanor.

So, ABC was pleased to award us a contract to do two more. By now, they could see our plan and were not quite as incredulous as to why we wanted world theatrical rights to mere television shows.

It was apparent that both new shows must be shot one after the other or "back to back." As *Eden* took place entirely in

*Mildred Natwick, Truman Capote's choice for Miriam,
with the author and Frank Perry*

a cemetery, we could not plan to shoot before May, lest the actors freeze attempting to recreate a "gentle spring day."

Casting went smoothly with the exception of Martin Balsam. Although he loved the script, he was starring on Broadway in *You Know I Can't Hear You When the Water's Running,* and felt that the strain of eight performances a week, plus acting in front of the cameras all day, *plus* the brutal trip to and from the film location outside Manhattan would be too much. I was finally able to persuade him by providing a mobile home, equipped with a Swedish masseuse to pick him up each morning and drive him to the theater from the set each night. On both trips, he was to receive her not so gentle but relaxing ministrations. We delighted in Marty's descriptions of the facial expressions of truck drivers who, at seven thirty in the morning, would peer down from the heights of their cabs through the half-opened curtains of the mobile home's bedroom suite to see the muscular lady at work on the well-oiled chest of an apparently naked man.

Our only other difficulty was getting permission to use the necessary cemetery. We needed as an integral part of the *mise en scène,* the direct visual juxtaposition of tombstones with the Manhattan skyline. Months of scouting had convinced us that only one cemetery was really the right one—Calvary in Queens. The Catholic Church was not about to let a group of moviemakers into their showplace cemetery. Once again, Capote came to the rescue with a few discreet phone calls to friends who "knew the Cardinal socially," and permission was ours.

In scouting the locations, I felt that one of the more interesting visually was the well-known Jewish cemetery, also in Queens. This is the one bisected by the Long Island Expressway, near the site of the World's Fair. As the skyline of Manhattan was not visible, I could not set the film here—but decided anyway to use shots of this one under titles—because of the great density of the stones and the gray, depressing aspect of the place. It was here we noticed each of the walks was marked by blue and white signs, which are used in our title shots: Path 11, Path 48, etc. I thought this was a nice artistic coincidence. Months

Among the Paths to Eden: *Martin Balsam and Maureen Stapleton in a cemetery in Queens*

later, I learned from Truman that it certainly was not a coincidence. The title for the story had suggested itself to him from these same signs in this same Queens cemetery.

Shooting on *Miriam* and *Eden* was completed in late June of 1967, and I spent the summer cutting both films. They were turned over to ABC in October. Then began the fascinating and absorbing task of combining our three fifty-two-minute television programs into *Trilogy*.

I spent the winter in New York, carefully whittling to bring our one hundred and fifty-six minutes down to proper feature-film length, which I judged to be about one hundred and ten minutes. It was also necessary to devise new main and end titles for the film, to optically effect the transitions from story to story as smoothly as possible, to create new music cues where scene and dialogue cuts affected old cues and so on.

From the beginning I had wanted to launch *Trilogy* at a major European film festival—hopefully at Cannes. Accordingly, I was pushing myself and the various laboratories involved to have the film ready to show to the selection committee of the festival. With a barely dry copy of the first answer print, we got on a plane for Paris in February, 1968. The committee, headed by M. Favre Le Bret, director of the festival, saw the film and was most complimentary. However, they could not reach a final decision until mid-April—and there were "dozens" of promising American films being offered for the two available slots for "Official American Entries." We'd simply have to wait. And home we went. And waited.

In mid-April it was announced in Paris that the two American entries at Cannes were *Trilogy* and *Petulia*. Surely the first time in the history of film that an official entry at Cannes from a major filmmaking country was, in fact, put together from materials made initially for television.

Truman came with us to the festival—and then the student revolution struck. *Trilogy*, scheduled in the final week of the festival, was never shown. We were left with our eight hundred sets of still photographs, our two thousand richly embossed brochures, our expensively subtitled print, our thousand-odd copies of translations of plot synopses into six languages and our various and assorted bills for these and other festival expenditures which ran well into five figures.

As this is written in January of 1969, *Trilogy* is scheduled to open in New York this fall. And we three, who seem to have formed a trilogy of our own, are at work on a new film. Which might very well be the beginning of a second trilogy. . . .

TRILOGY

some notes on adaptation by Eleanor Perry

ASSUMING the creative talent, it seems to me two things are extremely important in developing an ability to adapt literary material to film: one, a really deep empathy with the material, the author's theme, intention and view of life; and two, an unblocked imagination which is able to flow freely from the original source, playing, embroidering, ornamenting, extending and, in the most successful adaptations, even enriching the original material.

It has been pointed out that the more "literary" the primary story, the more difficult it is to adapt. A piece which depends for its effect on a brilliant style, on ideas, on interior monologues, on metaphor is often a disappointment on the screen. Similarly excellent films have been made from badly written books. In the first case the adapter has had to subtract, in the second he has added.

Many novels seem to be already written as scenarios—they are full of scenes, dramatic confrontation, incidents, dialogue. In some cases all the adapter has to do is to transpose the material into filmic terms, probably cutting, compressing and adding transitions. In other cases a book is in effect only a launching platform and a vast amount of creativity is necessary.

When we say an adaptation is good we can mean that it

A Christmas Memory

is faithful to the book and therefore has all the virtues of the book, that it has used the original author's premise with skill so that the extension is clever or sensitive or exciting or whatever, or we can mean that the adaptation *works*. To the people in the audience, unfamiliar with the primary source, this last is all that matters. Actually it is all that should matter to anyone. We look at a film as a film not as a piece of fiction transposed to another medium.

There is no particular technique of adaptation. There is no standard form. The adapter can use any device or style his imagination comes up with—the fresher the better. One cannot say "you must use a flashback there" or "you must use voice-over here." There is no must. The only limit on ways of telling the story is the almost unlimited and miraculous uses of the camera and the only test is "does it work?"

When the results are good it is extremely difficult to separate the contributions of the writer and director. It is much easier to tell what each has done when the results are bad. One can hear inept, awkward, unlikely dialogue, one can tell when characters are one dimensional or behave in ways which violate their reality—and one can nail the writer for it.

Scripts are written these days in what are called "master scenes." The writer used to put in every shot: "close up," "we pan with her," "tracking shot," "medium two shot," etc. By doing so, the writer was, in effect, directing the film. These days if a writer does put all that in the director will probably throw it all out. The only time it is useful is when.the writer really feels he has a brilliant idea or is using a certain angle or shot to help him tell the story. Today there is no particular mystique about the technical aspects of writing for film. One simply describes whatever one wants to without worrying about technical terms for the camera.

The best way to learn how to write films is to watch a lot of them and to see the good ones several times over. How to get in and out of flash-forwards or flashbacks or fantasies, how to use dialogue cuts, how to make visual cuts interesting, how to pace one's script, how to compress, how to use visuals to tell the story, how important human behavior is, how many lines of dialogue can be cut—acted rather than spoken, the vast emotional repertoire of the human face—all this will be demonstrated right on the screen.

Films can be studied on television, but it is more valuable in some ways to see them in theaters with an audience. One can learn a lot from the audience—primarily that it must not be underrated, or ever patronized. Audiences are sharper, brighter, more sensitive and aware than they have been in the past. Above all they have fantastic antennae when it comes to recognizing what is phony or fraudulent. They don't want anything spelled out in primer terms. They welcome the challenge of ambiguity, of leaving the theater with something to think about, argue about. Almost everyone hates being confused for the sake of being confused, but audiences today are willing not to understand everything immediately, are willing to go along with new techniques of cutting for example, or having their time sense temporarily disoriented as a story is told a new way.

If there is a difference between the mass audience which watches television and the "art-film" audience, I suppose it is in degrees of sophistication, but I don't feel that this should influence the way the writer handles his material. There is no difference in the basic humanity of any audience and a good film is a good film no matter what screen it is on.

Miriam
the story

For several years, Mrs. H. T. Miller had lived alone in a pleasant apartment (two rooms with kitchenette) in a remodeled brownstone near the East River. She was a widow: Mr. H. T. Miller had left a reasonable amount of insurance. Her interests were narrow, she had no friends to speak of, and she rarely journeyed farther than the corner grocery. The other people in the house never seemed to notice her: her clothes were matter-of-fact, her hair iron-gray, clipped and casually waved; she did not use cosmetics, her features were plain and inconspicuous, and on her last birthday she was sixty-one. Her activities were seldom spontaneous: she kept the two rooms immaculate, smoked an occasional cigarette, prepared her own meals and tended a canary.

Then she met Miriam. It was snowing that night. Mrs. Miller had finished drying the supper dishes and was thumbing through an afternoon paper when she saw an advertisement of a picture playing at a neighborhood theater. The title sounded good, so she struggled into her beaver coat, laced her galoshes and left the apartment, leaving one light burning in the foyer: she found nothing more disturbing than a sensation of darkness.

The snow was fine, falling gently, not yet making an impression on the pavement. The wind from the river cut only at street crossings. Mrs. Miller hurried, her head bowed, oblivious as a mole burrowing a blind path. She stopped at a drugstore and bought a package of peppermints.

A long line stretched in front of the box office; she took her place at the end. There would be (a tired voice groaned) a short wait for all seats. Mrs. Miller rummaged in her leather handbag till she collected exactly the correct change for admission. The line seemed to be taking its own time and, looking around for some distraction, she suddenly became conscious of a little girl standing under the edge of the marquee.

Her hair was the longest and strangest Mrs. Miller had ever seen: absolutely silver-white, like an albino's. It flowed waist-length in smooth, loose lines. She was thin and fragilely constructed. There was a simple, special elegance in the way she stood with her thumbs in the pockets of a tailored plum-velvet coat.

Mrs. Miller felt oddly excited, and when the little girl glanced toward her, she smiled warmly. The little girl walked over and said, "Would you care to do me a favor?"

"I'd be glad to, if I can," said Mrs. Miller.

"Oh, it's quite easy. I merely want you to buy a ticket for me; they won't let me in otherwise. Here, I have the money." And gracefully she handed Mrs. Miller two dimes and a nickel.

They went over to the theater together. An usherette directed them to a lounge; in twenty minutes the picture would be over.

"I feel just like a genuine criminal," said Mrs. Miller gaily, as she sat down. "I mean that sort of thing's against the law, isn't it? I do hope I haven't done the wrong thing. Your mother knows where you are, dear? I mean she does, doesn't she?"

The little girl said nothing. She unbuttoned her coat and folded it across her lap. Her dress underneath was prim and dark blue. A gold chain dangled about her neck, and her fingers, sensitive and musical-looking, toyed with it. Examining her more attentively, Mrs. Miller decided the truly distinctive feature was not her hair, but her eyes; they were hazel, steady, lacking any childlike quality whatsoever and, because of their size, seemed to consume her small face.

Mrs. Miller offered a peppermint. "What's your name, dear?"

"Miriam," she said, as though, in some curious way, it were information already familiar.

"Why, isn't that funny—my name's Miriam, too. And it's not a terribly common name either. Now, don't tell me your last name's Miller!"

"Just Miriam."

"But isn't that funny?"

"Moderately," said Miriam, and rolled the peppermint on her tongue.

Mrs. Miller flushed and shifted uncomfortably. "You have such a large vocabulary for such a little girl."

"Do I?"

"Well, yes," said Mrs. Miller, hastily changing the topic to: "Do you like the movies?"

"I really wouldn't know," said Miriam. "I've never been before."

Women began filling the lounge; the rumble of the newsreel bombs exploded in the distance. Mrs. Miller rose, tucking her purse under her arm. "I guess I'd better be running now if I want to get a seat," she said. "It was nice to have met you."

Miriam nodded ever so slightly.

It snowed all week. Wheels and footsteps moved soundlessly on the street, as if the business of living continued secretly behind a pale but impenetrable curtain. In the falling quiet there was no sky or earth, only snow lifting in the wind, frosting the window glass, chilling the rooms, deadening and hushing the city. At all hours it was necessary to keep a lamp lighted, and Mrs. Miller lost track of the days: Friday was no different from Saturday and on Sunday she went to the grocery: closed, of course.

That evening she scrambled eggs and fixed a bowl of tomato soup. Then, after putting on a flannel robe and cold-creaming her face, she propped herself up in bed with a hot-water bottle under her feet. She was reading the *Times* when the doorbell rang. At first she thought it must be a mistake and whoever it was would go away. But it rang and rang and settled to a persistent buzz. She looked at the clock: a little after eleven; it did not seem possible, she was always asleep by ten.

Climbing out of bed, she trotted barefoot across the living room. "I'm coming, please be patient." The latch was caught;

she turned it this way and that way and the bell never paused an instant. "Stop it," she cried. The bolt gave way and she opened the door an inch. "What in heaven's name?"

"Hello," said Miriam.

"Oh . . . why, hello," said Mrs. Miller, stepping hesitantly into the hall. "You're that little girl."

"I thought you'd never answer, but I kept my finger on the button; I knew you were home. Aren't you glad to see me?"

Mrs. Miller did not know what to say. Miriam, she saw, wore the same plum-velvet coat and now she had also a beret to match; her white hair was braided in two shining plaits and looped at the ends with enormous white ribbons.

"Since I've waited so long, you could at least let me in," she said.

"It's awfully late. . . ."

Miriam regarded her blankly. "What difference does that make? Let me in. It's cold out here and I have on a silk dress." Then, with a gentle gesture, she urged Mrs. Miller aside and passed into the apartment.

She dropped her coat and beret on a chair. She was indeed wearing a silk dress. White silk. White silk in February. The skirt was beautifully pleated and the sleeves long; it made a faint rustle as she strolled about the room. "I like your place," she said. "I like the rug, blue's my favorite color." She touched a paper rose in a vase on the coffee table. "Imitation," she commented wanly. "How sad. Aren't imitations sad?" She seated herself on the sofa, daintily spreading her skirt.

"What do you want?" asked Mrs. Miller.

"Sit down," said Miriam. "It makes me nervous to see people stand."

Mrs. Miller sank to a hassock. "What do you want?" she repeated.

"You know, I don't think you're glad I came."

For a second time Mrs. Miller was without an answer; her hand motioned vaguely. Miriam giggled and pressed back on a mound of chintz pillows. Mrs. Miller observed that the girl was less pale than she remembered; her cheeks were flushed.

"How did you know where I lived?"

Miriam frowned. "That's no question at all. What's your name? What's mine?"

"But I'm not listed in the phone book."

"Oh, let's talk about something else."

Mrs. Miller said, "Your mother must be insane to let a child like you wander around at all hours of the night—and in such ridiculous clothes. She must be out of her mind."

Miriam got up and moved to a corner where a covered bird cage hung from a ceiling chain. She peeked beneath the cover. "It's a canary," she said. "Would you mind if I woke him? I'd like to hear him sing."

"Leave Tommy alone," said Mrs. Miller, anxiously. "Don't you dare wake him."

"Certainly," said Miriam. "But I don't see why I can't hear him sing." And then, "Have you anything to eat? I'm starving! Even milk and a jam sandwich would be fine."

"Look," said Mrs. Miller, arising from the hassock, "look —if I make some nice sandwiches will you be a good child and run along home? It's past midnight, I'm sure."

"It's snowing," reproached Miriam. "And cold and dark."

"Well, you shouldn't have come here to begin with," said Mrs. Miller, struggling to control her voice. "I can't help the weather. If you want anything to eat you'll have to promise to leave."

Miriam brushed a braid against her cheek. Her eyes were thoughtful, as if weighing the proposition. She turned toward the bird cage. "Very well," she said, "I promise."

How old is she? Ten? Eleven? Mrs. Miller, in the kitchen, unsealed a jar of strawberry preserves and cut four slices of bread. She poured a glass of milk and paused to light a cigarette. *And why has she come?* Her hand shook as she held the match, fascinated, till it burned her finger. The canary was singing; singing as he did in the morning and at no other time. "Miriam," she called, "Miriam, I told you not to disturb Tommy." There was no answer. She called again; all she heard was the canary. She inhaled the cigarette and discovered she had lighted the cork-tip end and—oh, really, she mustn't lose her temper.

She carried the food in on a tray and set it on the coffee table. She saw first that the bird cage still wore its night cover. And Tommy was singing. It gave her a queer sensation. And no one was in the room. Mrs. Miller went through an alcove leading to her bedroom; at the door she caught her breath.

"What are you doing?" she asked.

Miriam glanced up and in her eyes there was a look that was not ordinary. She was standing by the bureau, a jewel case opened before her. For a minute she studied Mrs. Miller, forcing their eyes to meet, and she smiled. "There's nothing good here," she said. "But I like this." Her hand held a cameo brooch. "It's charming."

"Suppose—perhaps you'd better put it back," said Mrs. Miller, feeling suddenly the need of some support. She leaned against the door frame; her head was unbearably heavy; a pressure weighted the rhythm of her heartbeat. The light seemed to flutter defectively. "Please, child—a gift from my husband. . . ."

"But it's beautiful and I want it," said Miriam. *"Give it to me."*

As she stood, striving to shape a sentence which would somehow save the brooch, it came to Mrs. Miller there was no one to whom she might turn; she was alone; a fact that had not been among her thoughts for a long time. Its sheer emphasis was stunning. But here in her own room in the hushed snow-city were evidences she could not ignore or, she knew with startling clarity, resist.

Miriam ate ravenously, and when the sandwiches and milk were gone, her fingers made cobweb movements over the plate, gathering crumbs. The cameo gleamed on her blouse, the blond profile like a trick reflection of its wearer. "That was very nice," she sighed, "though now an almond cake or a cherry would be ideal. Sweets are lovely, don't you think?"

Mrs. Miller was perched precariously on the hassock, smoking a cigarette. Her hair net had slipped lopsided and loose strands straggled down her face. Her eyes were stupidly concentrated on nothing and her cheeks were mottled in red patches, as though a fierce slap had left permanent marks.

"Is there a candy—a cake?"

Mrs. Miller tapped ash on the rug. Her head swayed slightly as she tried to focus her eyes. "You promised to leave if I made the sandwiches," she said.

"Dear me, did I?"

"It was a promise and I'm tired and I don't feel well at all."

"Mustn't fret," said Miriam. "I'm only teasing."

She picked up her coat, slung it over her arm, and arranged her beret in front of a mirror. Presently she bent close to Mrs. Miller and whispered, "Kiss me good night."

"Please—I'd rather not," said Mrs. Miller.

Miriam lifted a shoulder, arched an eyebrow. "As you like," she said, and went directly to the coffee table, seized the vase containing the paper roses, carried it to where the hard surface of the floor lay bare, and hurled it downward. Glass sprayed in all directions and she stamped her foot on the bouquet.

Then slowly she walked to the door, but before closing it she looked back at Mrs. Miller with a slyly innocent curiosity.

Mrs. Miller spent the next day in bed, rising once to feed the canary and drink a cup of tea; she took her temperature and had none, yet her dreams were feverishly agitated; their unbalanced mood lingered even as she lay staring wide-eyed at the ceiling. One dream threaded through the others like an elusively mysterious theme in a complicated symphony, and the scenes it depicted were sharply outlined, as though sketched by a hand of gifted intensity: a small girl, wearing a bridal gown and a wreath of leaves, led a gray procession down a mountain path, and among them there was unusual silence till a woman at the rear asked, "Where is she taking us?" "No one knows," said an old man marching in front. "But isn't she pretty?" volunteered a third voice. "Isn't she like a frost flower . . . so shining and white?"

Tuesday morning she woke up feeling better; harsh slats of sunlight, slanting through Venetian blinds, shed a disrupting light on her unwholesome fancies. She opened the window to discover a thawed, mild-as-spring day; a sweep of clean new clouds crumpled against a vastly blue, out-of-season sky; and across the low line of rooftops she could see the river and smoke curving from tugboat stacks in a warm wind. A great silver truck plowed the snow-banked street, its machine sound humming on the air.

After straightening the apartment, she went to the grocer's, cashed a check and continued to Schrafft's where she ate breakfast and chatted happily with the waitress. Oh, it was a wonderful day—more like a holiday—and it would be so foolish to go home.

She boarded a Lexington Avenue bus and rode up to Eighty-sixth Street; it was here that she had decided to do a little shopping.

She had no idea what she wanted or needed, but she idled along, intent only upon the passers-by, brisk and preoccupied, who gave her a disturbing sense of separateness.

It was while waiting at the corner of Third Avenue that she saw the man: an old man, bowlegged and stooped under an armload of bulging packages; he wore a shabby brown coat and a checkered cap. Suddenly she realized they were exchanging a smile: there was nothing friendly about this smile, it was merely two cold flickers of recognition. But she was certain she had never seen him before.

He was standing next to an El pillar, and as she crossed the street he turned and followed. He kept quite close; from the corner of her eye she watched his reflection wavering on the shopwindows.

Then in the middle of the block she stopped and faced him. He stopped also and cocked his head, grinning. But what could she say? Do? Here, in broad daylight, on Eighty-sixth Street? It was useless and, despising her own helplessness, she quickened her steps.

Now Second Avenue is a dismal street, made from scraps and ends; part cobblestone, part asphalt, part cement; and its atmosphere of desertion is permanent. Mrs. Miller walked five blocks without meeting anyone, and all the while the steady crunch of his footfalls in the snow stayed near. And when she came to a florist's shop, the sound was still with her. She hurried inside and watched through the glass door as the old man passed;

he kept his eyes straight ahead and didn't slow his pace, but he did one strange, telling thing: he tipped his cap.

"Six white ones, did you say?" asked the florist. "Yes," she told him, "white roses." From there she went to a glassware store and selected a vase, presumably a replacement for the one Miriam had broken, though the price was intolerable and the vase itself (she thought) grotesquely vulgar. But a series of unaccountable purchases had begun, as if by prearranged plan: a plan of which she had not the least knowledge or control.

She bought a bag of glazed cherries, and at a place called the Knickerbocker Bakery she paid forty cents for six almond cakes.

Within the last hour the weather had turned cold again; like blurred lenses, winter clouds cast a shade over the sun, and the skeleton of an early dusk colored the sky; a damp mist mixed with the wind and the voices of a few children who romped high on mountains of gutter snow seemed lonely and cheerless. Soon the first flake fell, and when Mrs. Miller reached the brownstone house, snow was falling in a swift screen and foot tracks vanished as they were printed.

The white roses were arranged decoratively in the vase. The glazed cherries shone on a ceramic plate. The almond cakes, dusted with sugar, awaited a hand. The canary fluttered on its swing and picked at a bar of seed.

At precisely five the doorbell rang. Mrs. Miller *knew* who it was. The hem of her housecoat trailed as she crossed the floor. "Is that you?" she called.

"Naturally," said Miriam, the word resounding shrilly from the hall. "Open this door."

"Go away," said Mrs. Miller.

"Please hurry . . . I have a heavy package."

"Go away," said Mrs. Miller. She returned to the living room, lighted a cigarette, sat down and calmly listened to the buzzer; on and on and on. "You might as well leave. I have no intention of letting you in."

Shortly the bell stopped. For possibly ten minutes Mrs.

Miller did not move. Then, hearing no sound, she concluded Miriam had gone. She tiptoed to the door and opened it a sliver; Miriam was half-reclining atop a cardboard box with a beautiful French doll cradled in her arms.

"Really, I thought you were never coming," she said peevishly. "Here, help me get this in, it's awfully heavy."

It was not spell-like compulsion that Mrs. Miller felt, but rather a curious passivity; she brought in the box, Miriam the doll. Miriam curled up on the sofa, not troubling to remove her coat or beret, and watched disinterestedly as Mrs. Miller dropped the box and stood trembling, trying to catch her breath.

"Thank you," she said. In the daylight she looked pinched and drawn, her hair less luminous. The French doll she was loving wore an exquisite powdered wig and its idiot glass eyes sought solace in Miriam's. "I have a surprise," she continued. "Look into my box."

Kneeling, Mrs. Miller parted the flaps and lifted out another doll; then a blue dress which she recalled as the one Miriam had worn that first night at the theater; and of the remainder she said, "It's all clothes. Why?"

"Because I've come to live with you," said Miriam, twisting a cherry stem. "Wasn't it nice of you to buy me the cherries . . .?"

"But you can't! For God's sake go away—go away and leave me alone!"

". . . and the roses and the almond cakes? How really wonderfully generous. You know, these cherries are delicious. The last place I lived was with an old man; he was terribly poor and we never had good things to eat. But I think I'll be happy here." She paused to snuggle her doll closer. "Now, if you'll just show me where to put my things. . . ."

Mrs. Miller's face dissolved into a mask of ugly red lines; she began to cry, and it was an unnatural, tearless sort of weeping, as though, not having wept for a long time, she had forgotten how. Carefully she edged backward till she touched the door.

She fumbled through the hall and down the stairs to a landing below. She pounded frantically on the door of the first apartment she came to; a short, redheaded man answered and she pushed past him. "Say, what the hell is this?" he said. "Anything wrong, lover?" asked a young woman who appeared from the kitchen, drying her hands. And it was to her that Mrs. Miller turned.

"Listen," she cried, "I'm ashamed behaving this way but —well, I'm Mrs. H. T. Miller and I live upstairs and . . . ." She pressed her hands over her face. "It sounds so absurd . . . ."

The woman guided her to a chair, while the man excitedly rattled pocket change. "Yeah?"

"I live upstairs and there's a little girl visiting me, and I suppose that I'm afraid of her. She won't leave and I can't make her and—she's going to do something terrible. She's already stolen my cameo, but she's about to do something worse—something terrible!"

The man asked, "Is she a relative, huh?"

Mrs. Miller shook her head. "I don't know who she is. Her name's Miriam, but I don't know for certain who she is."

"You gotta calm down, honey," said the woman, stroking Mrs. Miller's arm. "Harry here'll tend to this kid. Go on, lover." And Mrs. Miller said, "The door's open—5A."

After the man left, the woman brought a towel and bathed Mrs. Miller's face. "You're very kind," Mrs. Miller said. "I'm sorry to act like such a fool, only this wicked child . . . ."

"Sure, honey," consoled the woman. "Now, you better take it easy."

Mrs. Miller rested her head in the crook of her arm; she was quiet enough to be asleep. The woman turned a radio dial; a piano and a husky voice filled the silence and the woman, tapping her foot, kept excellent time. "Maybe we oughta go up too," she said.

"I don't want to see her again. I don't want to be anywhere near her."

"Uh huh, but what you shoulda done, you shoulda called a cop."

Presently they heard the man on the stairs. He strode into the room frowning and scratching the back of his neck. "Nobody there," he said, honestly embarrassed. "She musta beat it."

"Harry, you're a jerk," announced the woman. "We been

sitting here the whole time and we woulda seen . . ." she stopped abruptly, for the man's glance was sharp.

"I looked all over," he said, "and there just ain't nobody there. Nobody, understand?"

"Tell me," said Mrs. Miller, rising, "tell me, did you see a large box? Or a doll?"

"No, ma'am, I didn't."

And the woman, as if delivering a verdict, said, "Well, for cryinoutloud . . . ."

Mrs. Miller entered her apartment softly; she walked to the center of the room and stood quite still. No, in a sense it had not changed: the roses, the cakes, and the cherries were in place. But this was an empty room, emptier than if the furnishings and familiars were not present, lifeless and petrified as a funeral parlor. The sofa loomed before her with a new strangeness: its vacancy had a meaning that would have been less penetrating and terrible had Miriam been curled on it. She gazed fixedly at the space where she remembered setting the box and, for a moment, the hassock spun desperately. And she looked through the window; surely the river was real, surely snow was falling—but then, one could not be certain witness to anything: Miriam, so vividly there—and yet, where was she? Where, where?

As though moving in a dream, she sank to a chair. The room was losing shape; it was dark and getting darker and there was nothing to be done about it; she could not lift her hand to light a lamp.

Suddenly, closing her eyes, she felt an upward surge, like a diver emerging from some deeper, greener depth. In times of terror or immense distress, there are moments when the mind waits, as though for a revelation, while a skein of calm is woven over thought; it is like a sleep, or a supernatural trance; and during this lull one is aware of a force of quiet reasoning: well, what if she had never really known a girl named Miriam? that she had been foolishly frightened on the street? In the end, like everything else, it was of no importance. For the only thing she had lost to Miriam was her identity, but now she knew she had found again the person who lived in this room, who cooked her own meals, who owned a canary, who was someone she could trust and believe in: Mrs. H. T. Miller.

Listening in contentment, she became aware of a double sound: a bureau drawer opening and closing; she seemed to hear it long after completion—opening and closing. Then gradually, the harshness of it was replaced by the murmur of a silk dress and this, delicately faint, was moving nearer and swelling in intensity till the walls trembled with the vibration and the room was caving under a wave of whispers. Mrs. Miller stiffened and opened her eyes to a full, direct stare.

"Hello," said Miriam.

Miriam

the script

FADE IN:

A model sailboat with bright red sails floats becalmed on limpid blue water. As CAMERA begins a slow zoom back, we see a soft, melted bronze blurred image of what might be a little girl's head. Continue this almost imperceptible PULLBACK, WIDENING SHOT to reveal full figure of the girl (still in extremely soft focus and not yet identifiable), seated on a low chair of some sort. Now, as the SHOT continues to WIDEN, looming behind her is a gigantic figure—perhaps a top-hatted animal on haunch.

Now, faintly, the sound of children playing. Blurs of movement in front of our lens too close to be identifiable as anything but streaks. Movement too, behind the central figures of the seated girl and standing animal, also blurred but, now, seemingly, a relationship has begun between the moving blurs and the sound of children playing.

As the SHOT continues to WIDEN and the CAMERA begins a long, circular TRACKING SHOT, we gently and slowly resolve focus to reveal: the giant bronze sculptured group of "Alice in Wonderland" figures in Central Park, adjacent to the model sailboat pool.

As focus continues to resolve, we see that children are running, laughing, playing, climbing on the statues, attended, watched over, by a seated circle of dutiful nursemaids who mind their baby carriages while nodding and gossiping one to the other.

After the scene is fully established, a ball comes bouncing and rolling toward the CAMERA. Chasing it is a pretty little girl with long blond hair, wearing a pinafore, who runs into a FULL SHOT and then suddenly looks up, startled, frowning, and perhaps just a little bit frightened as we

SLAM CUT TO:

EXTREME CLOSE UP. Miss Miller's smiling face.

> MISS MILLER
> I've got your ball! I've got your ball! Now what are you going to do, honeybunch?

The little girl's frown deepens.

> MISS MILLER
> Maybe if you're a very good little girl and give your old Nanny a kiss she'll give the ball back.

> LITTLE GIRL
> You're not my nanny!

She runs to a young woman in a nurse's uniform who is sitting on a bench nearby. The nurse's name is Miss Lake.

> MISS LAKE
> What's the matter, Emily?

> LITTLE GIRL
> She stole my ball!

Miss Miller crosses to the bench. She is in her early sixties, pleasant looking, although at times a strange anxious expression comes into her eyes. Her voice is cultivated but she has an artificially high tone she uses when addressing children or talking about them. She is wearing a coat and hat which are the essence of shabby respectability.

> MISS MILLER
> Oh dear, oh dear, what a funny little thing. She thinks I'm a thief. Here is your ball honeybunch, I was only playing.

Emily takes the ball.

> MISS LAKE
> You see Emily, the lady was only playing . . .
> *(To Miss Miller)*
> You must excuse her. She's very shy.

> MISS MILLER
> Oh I know, I know. I'm used to little ones. I've
> taken care of them all my life. As a matter of fact,
> haven't we met before?

> MISS LAKE
> I don't . . . think so.

> MISS MILLER
> *(sitting beside her)*
> When I nursed the Pritchards' children I spent many
> an hour on this very spot. The Stuyvesant
> Pritchards. You must know them.

> MISS LAKE
> *(politely)*
> I don't believe so, no.

Miss Miller opens her purse and takes out a package of Life Savers. She offers them to Miss Lake who shakes her head and smiles.

> MISS MILLER
> Very prominent people. Very prominent indeed.
> Mrs. Pritchard was a Chisholm girl. The Woodrow
> Chisholms. You know who *they* are, of course?

> MISS LAKE
> No . . . I'm sorry . . .

> MISS MILLER
> Who they were, I should say. Both passed on years
> ago. That's where the Pritchards' money comes
> from. *Her* side. We used to spend every summer in
> the south of France. I tell you I was glad to get
> back to the land of the free and the home of the
> brave. You can say what you want about French
> cooking, but I'll take my egg and my tea
> anytime . . .

MISS LAKE
Get your ball, Emily, we've got to go now . . .

She is obviously eager to get away.

MISS MILLER
Then there were the Dunlaps just two blocks away . . .
very colicky baby, that little Chester Dunlap.
Mrs. Dunlap was always bringing her guests in to
see the baby, breathing their gin cocktails all over
him. He was tipsy just from smelling their
breaths . . . but of course we had to call it colic . . .

Miss Lake takes Emily's ball. Emily climbs on her tricycle.

MISS LAKE
Well we're headed for home . . . so nice to have
talked with you . . .

MISS MILLER
(*joining her*)
I'll walk along with you. I have an appointment at
four right in that building on the corner.

*This clearly doesn't please Miss Lake, but there seems to be no
way to decline politely. They walk along together, the little girl
riding in front.*

MISS MILLER
I'm having tea with Mrs. Terrance Packard. She
was Nina Whitfield when I met her. Must be
twenty years ago. Time certainly flies, doesn't it?

MISS LAKE
Oh my, yes . . .

MISS MILLER
Just to think . . . My little baby Nina—all grown
up and going to have a baby of her own. And
nothing will do except that I come back and nurse
Nina's baby!

MISS LAKE
How nice for you.

MISS MILLER
I wouldn't do it for anyone but Nina. I've been
retired for almost two years now. But Nina insists.
She says she simply can't have this baby without
her old Nanny by her side. So I'll get the little
one off to a good start and then I'll help her find
someone competent and conscientious like myself.
(peering at Miss Lake)
You're not thinking of making a change in—
oh, six months, are you?

MISS LAKE
Oh, no. I'm very happy with the Brooks family.

MISS MILLER
I could recommend you highly to Mrs. Packard.

MISS LAKE
Thank you very much, but—

MISS MILLER
Of course, I don't really know you. Perhaps we
could have tea together Thursday and get
acquainted in a friendly way . . .

MISS LAKE
(the last thing on earth she wants to do)
I really can't make it on Thursday . . .

MISS MILLER
(eagerly)
What about Sunday? Come to my apartment. You
can meet Tommy—that's my canary. I know where
to get some perfectly lovely tea cakes—vanilla eclairs
that just melt in your mouth. We can have a cozy
chat and then maybe go to the movies afterwards . . .

MISS LAKE
I'm very sorry, but I have an engagement on
Sunday.

She takes Emily by the hand and hurries off.

MISS MILLER
They're very prominent people . . . Nina worships
the ground I walk on.

CLOSE SHOT. Nina.

She opens an apartment door. She is a young woman of twenty-two, beautifully dressed and six months pregnant.

> NINA
> (*surprised*)
> Why Nanny!

> MISS MILLER
> Honeybunch! How are you?

> NINA
> Oh Nanny, you'll have to forgive me . . . I
> completely forgot you were going to stop in
> today . . .

> MISS MILLER
> Of course I'll forgive you. I know how much you
> have on your mind—packing up for the country
> and all . . .

> NINA
> (*still in the doorway*)
> Nanny, I'm so sorry I've made an appointment.
> I was just getting ready to leave.

> MISS MILLER
> (*she steps around her into the foyer*)
> Oh well, you can spare five minutes for your old
> Nanny, can't you?

Miss Miller crosses into the luxurious living room. Nina follows reluctantly.

> NINA
> It's a doctor's appointment. I really ought to go
> right now . . .

> MISS MILLER
> (*gazing around the room*)
> Doctors never see anyone on time. Might as well
> wait here as in his waiting room . . . what a lovely
> room. Lovely!

She sits on the couch as if settling down for a long visit. Nina sits on the edge of a chair.

MISS MILLER
(reproachfully)
You've been married two years, honeybunch, and
you've never invited me to tea.
(she leans forward)
What a lucky thing I ran into Mummy the other
day or I'd never have known about the baby until
too late . . .

NINA
Too late?

MISS MILLER
I might have taken another position and think what
a mess that would have been. As you know I'm not
the kind to leave people once I've given my word.
One thing you know about your old Nanny—
she's loyal. Loyal and devoted.

Nina reaches for a cigarette.

MISS MILLER
(as if to a five-year-old)
Oh no, honeybunch! No! No! Bad for the baby!

NINA
(firmly)
Listen, Nanny, there's something we have to
straighten out right now . . . I've already engaged
a nurse for the baby.

MISS MILLER
You what?
(aghast)
What do you mean?

NINA
I'm terribly sorry if you thought . . . . There's
nothing I can do about it now.

MISS MILLER
But . . . what nurse? Who is she? Oh honeybunch,
you'll just have to call her up and tell her your old
Nanny's coming back.
(she is close to tears)

NINA

I really can't. It's all been arranged and settled.

MISS MILLER

Oh dear, oh dear, oh dear . . . this really is a shock!
Here I am willing to come out of *retirement* for
you . . . be at your side . . . take over for you . . .

NINA
(gently)
After the first few weeks I'm going to take care of
the baby myself.

MISS MILLER

Oh, don't be silly. What do you know about babies?

NINA

I'll learn, Nanny. I want to.

MISS MILLER

Oh my goodness, Nina, I've been counting on . . .
you simply must find that nurse another position . . .

NINA

No, Nanny . . .

MISS MILLER
(on the edge of panic)
You *must!*

Sympathetically but firmly, Nina shakes her head.

CUT TO:

MISS MILLER'S APARTMENT

*Very modestly furnished, spinsterish-looking living room. A port-
able TV set in one corner, a canary in a cage, a vase of plastic
flowers on the coffee table. Everything is very neat but worn
looking. On a shelf are several framed photographs of children
of various ages—mostly babies, but some three, four, and five
years old. There are some newspaper photos of brides which
Miss Miller has cut out of the papers and framed.*

*Miss Miller is eating her dinner—out of the typical square sec-
tioned tray that contains a frozen TV dinner. She is sitting at a
gate-legged table, consulting the newspaper while she dines. The*

canary, whose name is Tommy, swings in its cage nearby. Its activity attracts Miss Miller's attention. She looks up at the canary.

> MISS MILLER
>
> Go on now, Tommy. I want you to take your bath.
> Nanny put a dish of nice clean water there for you.

The canary blinks at her and hops about.

> MISS MILLER
>
> Hurry up now. Nanny's going to the movies
> tonight and you have to be all bathed and shiny
> clean before she goes. Hmmn?

The phone rings. Miss Miller crosses and picks it up.

> MISS MILLER
> *(into phone)*
> Hello . . .
> *(then indignantly)*
> *What did you say?* . . . Exactly whom are you
> calling? . . . Me! But that's impossible, you don't
> know me!
> *(angrily)*
> Who is this? Who are you? . . . I *beg* your pardon?
> *(aghast)*
> Why I certainly will *not*! Outrageous! You certainly
> have the *wrong number*!
> *(she hangs up furiously. To canary)*
> Can you *imagine*, Tommy? A perfectly strange man!
> He . . . he wanted me to meet him! In a *bar*!

No reaction from the canary. She picks up her teacup and starts towards the kitchen.

> MISS MILLER
> My, oh my, what's the world coming to!

CUT TO:

The exterior of a movie theater. It is a dark, misty night, raining slightly. Miss Miller joins a short line at the box office. She extracts the right change from her purse and while she is waiting, glances around. She notices standing nearby, a small girl, perhaps ten or eleven. She wears a raincoat and her hair is tucked up under a sou'wester rain hat. Her face is expressionless, a little tired, thin, ageless and very pale. She is staring fixedly at Miss Miller. Their eyes meet for a moment and then she crosses to Miss Miller.

> GIRL
> Excuse me—

> MISS MILLER
> Yes?

> GIRL
> *(offering Miss Miller a bill)*
> Please, would you buy me a ticket?

> MISS MILLER
> Me? I don't understand

> GIRL
> It's after six o'clock. They don't admit children after six unless accompanied by an adult.
> *(as Miss Miller hesitates)*
> Please.

> MISS MILLER
> *(uncertainly)*
> Well . . . I don't suppose there's any harm in your seeing a Western, is there?

> GIRL
> No, why should there be?

INTERIOR OF THEATER

Miss Miller and the little girl are going down the stairs to the lounge.

> MISS MILLER
> *(as she folds up her plastic rainhood)*
> I must say, I love the movies! I love sitting in the dark and just forgetting about everything except what's up there on the screen.

THEATER LOUNGE

They sit down on a couch in the lounge. A few other people are scattered about drinking coffee which is served by a waitress at the other end of the lounge. The little girl pops a Life Saver into her mouth. Then she takes off her rain hat and an abundance of long pale golden hair falls to her shoulders.

> MISS MILLER
> My, but you have lovely hair! . . . Beautiful color!

Girl's hair is parted on the side and fastened with a barrette. She reaches up to adjust the barrette.

> MISS MILLER
> You may not believe this but when I was a child, my hair looked exactly the same. I wore it very much like that. What's your name, honeybunch?

> GIRL
> Miriam.

> MISS MILLER
> *(excited)*
> Miriam? Really and truly? Isn't that an interesting coincidence? My name is Miriam, too. But I forget about it sometimes because nobody's called me that for years . . . everybody calls me Nanny or Miss Miller.

> MIRIAM
> Why don't you have a cup of coffee, Miriam?

> MISS MILLER
> *(rising)*
> Yes . . . I think I will.
> *(then, suddenly)*
> I'll let it go this time, but young people mustn't call grown-ups by their first names. That's not respectful.

Miriam smiles remotely and pops another Life Saver into her mouth.

Miss Miller crosses to the waitress and picks up a demitasse. She carries it back to the couch. Since her eyes are on the cup to see that the coffee doesn't spill she doesn't notice until she is practically there that Miriam is nowhere in sight. Miss Miller turns to a Man sitting nearby.

> MISS MILLER
> Excuse me, did you see a child? . . . A little girl? . . .

> MAN
> A little girl?

> MISS MILLER
> . . . with long blonde hair? She was sitting
> right here.

> MAN
> I don't believe I noticed. No.

> MISS MILLER
> (*slightly upset*)
> I suppose she's gone inside.

She puts the coffee down untasted and hurries into the theater.

> CUT TO:

INT.: MISS MILLER'S APARTMENT

> MISS MILLER
> (*picks up a folded cloth*)
> Say good night to your old Nanny, Tommy.
> (*drapes the cloth over the cage*)
> Here comes the sandman to sprinkle sand in your
> eyes!
> (*doorbell rings insistently*)
> My . . . Who in the world can that be?
> (*another insistent peal from the bell*)
> Somebody's made a mistake. We certainly aren't
> expecting callers at this hour of the night.
> (*bell now rings continuously as if someone
> is holding a finger down on it*)
> Goodness, what a racket! How's Tommy going to
> get to sleep with a racket like that going on?

*She drapes the cloth all the way over the cage and crosses to the
door. She unlocks it, leaving the chain on, and opens it just a
crack. Miriam is standing in the hall, her raincoat and hat drip-
ping wet.*

> MIRIAM
> Hello.

MISS MILLER
Good heavens, what are you doing here?

MIRIAM
Let me in. I'm cold.

Miss Miller unclasps the chain and opens the door. Miriam walks in.

MISS MILLER
(*shocked*)
Wandering around in the rain at this hour of the night! Your parents must be mad to allow you to be out this late. Do your parents know where you are?

She helps Miriam off with her coat and hat and hangs them on a chair to dry. Miriam is wearing a white silk dress, finely made with a slightly old-fashioned air to its cut and fit. Whenever she moves we hear the rustling sound of the white silk.

MISS MILLER
What a lovely dress! Imagine wearing a dress like that just to go to the movies in the rain.

MIRIAM
White is my favorite color. White stands for purity, you know.
(*she looks around*)
I like your apartment. It's very neat and comfortable.

She strolls about the room examining the objects in it.

MISS MILLER
What happened to you in the movie theater?
I couldn't find you anywhere.

Miriam stops before the vase of plastic flowers on the coffee table. She touches them.

MIRIAM
I don't like these. They're imitations. Imitations of anything make me feel sad.

MISS MILLER
How did you know where I lived? Did you follow me home? I didn't see you following me . . .

Miriam ignores her questions and continues around the room. She stops in front of the shelves of photographs and studies them.

MISS MILLER
Aren't they dears? My little lambs!

She fondles a couple of the photographs affectionately. Miriam picks up a photograph and examines it.

MISS MILLER
(*eagerly*)
That's little Nina Whitfield—Nina Packard she is now. All grown up . . . going to have a baby of her own.

MIRIAM
She looks mean.

MISS MILLER
Oh no! She has the face of a little angel!

MIRIAM
Mean and selfish.

MISS MILLER
A bit high-spirited, maybe . . .
(*shows Miriam a photo of a bride*)
Here she is on her wedding day. I cut it out of the *Times*.

MIRIAM
Were you at her wedding?

MISS MILLER
Oh my yes. She wouldn't have allowed the ceremony to proceed without me there.

MIRIAM
Did she send you an invitation?

MISS MILLER
Why, of course she did.

Miriam turns her back on the shelf of photos and crosses to the canary's cage. She lifts an edge of the cloth.

MIRIAM
Your bird's sleeping.

MISS MILLER
I know. Please don't wake him, honeybunch.

MIRIAM
I want to hear him sing.

MISS MILLER
Well, maybe next time you come.

MIRIAM
Oh, then it's alright if I visit you again.

MISS MILLER
Oh yes, but not at this hour of the night.

MIRIAM
Do you like children?

MISS MILLER
What a question! I love children!

MIRIAM
Do you love them no matter what they do?

MISS MILLER
Unless they're naughty and tell fibs.

MIRIAM
Oh, then you're going to love me very much.
I always tell the truth.
    (smiles—a curious smile that never reaches
    her eyes)
Do you have any cake? I'd like a piece of cake
before I go.

MISS MILLER
Oh, what a pity. I didn't stop at the bakery today.

MIRIAM
Then I guess I might as well leave.

MISS MILLER
Would you like a nice bread and jelly sandwich
before you go?

MIRIAM

No, I like almond cakes or cherry tarts, or eclairs.
Vanilla eclairs are my favorites.

MISS MILLER

All right, honeybunch. I'll remember that.

As Miriam crosses toward the door she stops at the coffee table, picks up the vase of imitation flowers and hurls it to the floor. The glass vase crashes and shatters.

MISS MILLER
(*appalled*)
Miriam! Why did you do that?

MIRIAM
(*very cool*)
I told you. I don't like imitations.

MISS MILLER
(*indignant*)
You have no right to destroy something of mine,
no matter how you feel about it.

MIRIAM

Oh, you don't like imitations either. You just
pretend you do.

She gives Miss Miller her enigmatic smile as she goes out and closes the door.

HORN AND HARDART CAFETERIA. NIGHT.

Miss Miller, tray in hand, newspaper and umbrella under her arm, puts coins in one of the machines and removes a sandwich. Then she crosses to the tea spout, inserts coins and gets herself a cup of tea.

She starts through the cafeteria looking for a place to sit down. Finally she stops at a table for four occupied by a man and a woman, both obviously strangers to each other. The man, shabby and seedy with a day's growth of beard, has a cup of coffee in front of him and is staring into space. The woman is young, plump and overly made up. She is trying to eat a plate of spaghetti without messing up her lipstick. This causes her to make

peculiar facial contortions as she vacuums the spaghetti off her fork.

Miss Miller notices that the woman's purse and umbrella are on the third chair. She takes the fourth for herself, puts down her tray and hooks her own umbrella over the back of her chair. After a brief glance, the two strangers pay no attention to her.

> MISS MILLER
> *(genially)*
> I think we're in for a few showers, don't you?

They look at her without answering and look away again.

> MISS MILLER
> Just like last night. I went out to the movies in
> spite of the rain. A very exciting Western. In color.
> Of course, I had my raincoat and my rain hood on,
> so I didn't get wet.

She might as well be talking to a wall as far as reactions from her tablemates go.

> MISS MILLER
> Just before I left I got the strangest telephone call . . .
> *(leans toward the man)*
> To whom does one report those things, do you know?

The man stares into space.

> MISS MILLER
> Sir! *I'm asking you a question!*

The man turns to stare at her, the woman looks up, her fork halfway to her mouth.

> MAN
> What?

> MISS MILLER
> I had a telephone call from an absolute stranger
> asking me to meet him in a bar! I'd like to know
> what authorities to inform about that.

> MAN
> *(shaking his head, almost to himself)*
> Boy, oh boy, oh boy.

He gets up abruptly and leaves. Miss Miller looks after him with mild surprise.

> MISS MILLER
> (to the woman)
> Well, good riddance! It was a mistake to ask *his* advice!
> (chummily)
> Respectable women like you and me will have to take action.

The woman, after a quick suspicious glance at her, begins to eat her spaghetti more hastily.

> MISS MILLER
> These demented creatures with their rude invitations must be tracked down.
> (she leans over, very friendly)
> Do you think we should form a neighborhood committee?

The woman pushes aside her plate, grabs her purse and swiftly leaves the table. Again Miss Miller looks mildly surprised. Suddenly she notices the woman's umbrella left behind on the chair. She picks it up and looks after the rapidly retreating figure. She replaces the umbrella.

> MISS MILLER
> Miss . . . Miss . . . Miss . . . Oh well—she'll be back for it.

She starts to eat and read her paper. Suddenly we hear the rustle of silk and Miriam, her raincoat over her arm, slips into a chair at the table. Miss Miller is immersed in her newspaper, turning the pages rapidly. Miriam puts her elbows on the table, rests her chin in her hands.

> MIRIAM
> (always with the same tone and inflection)
> Hello!

Miss Miller looks up. Now she is surprised.

> MISS MILLER
> Goodness sake! What are you doing here?

Miriam takes out a package of Life Savers and pops one into her mouth.

MISS MILLER
Aren't you having anything?

MIRIAM
They don't have vanilla eclairs . . . I looked.

MISS MILLER
Honeybunch, you can't *live* on vanilla eclairs.

MIRIAM
You promised.

MISS MILLER
Well, I know I did. I meant I'd have them for you at home.

She turns a page of her paper and suddenly she gasps with pleasure.

MISS MILLER
Why look! It's Millicent Castle!

MIRIAM
(*reading*)
She's going to be married next Sunday.

MISS MILLER
Isn't that nice? Another lovely wedding to go to! . . . I must buy a new hat. Something with flowers I think, for a June wedding.

MIRIAM
How long has it been since you've heard from Millicent?

MISS MILLER
She's a flibberty-gibberty little thing. Young girls nowadays don't have time to make calls and pay visits. But a wedding is different. Why she wouldn't allow the ceremony to proceed without me.

Miriam smiles and slips into her coat. She sees the umbrella the woman has left behind on the chair and picks it up.

MISS MILLER
Miriam, what are you doing with that umbrella?

MIRIAM
I'm taking it with me.

MISS MILLER
But it doesn't belong to you. The woman who left it
will come back looking for it.

MIRIAM
That's too bad . . .
(*with a sly smile*)
It won't be here.

*She tucks the umbrella under her arm and crosses the restaurant
toward the door. Miss Miller looks after her with disapproval.*

MISS MILLER
Miriam! Miriam!

CUT TO:

MODEST LOBBY OF MISS MILLER'S BUILDING

*A row of 20 or 30 mailboxes in one wall. Miss Miller is at her
box. It is open and she is thrusting her hand into it. Obviously
it is empty and obviously she is annoyed. At this moment a
middle-aged couple enter from the outside. They are Mr. and
Mrs. Connolly, neighbors of Miss Miller.*

MRS. CONNOLLY
Good evening, Miss Miller.

MISS MILLER
Good evening, Mrs. Connolly; Mr. Connolly. You
two certainly are dressed up tonight!

MRS. CONNOLLY
We've been to a cocktail buffet . . . at the Stetsons'
Building . . .

MISS MILLER
The Stetsons? No, I—I don't think I know them.
Oh, by the way, Mrs. Connolly, I'm entertaining a
guest tonight. If you and Mr. Connolly would care
to drop in later for coffee and vanilla eclairs, I'd be
most pleased to have you . . .

MR. CONNOLLY

I'm sorry, Miss Miller, we've invited a couple of friends in for bridge.

MISS MILLER

Bring them along. We'll have a little get-together. Thank heaven the shops are still open . . . I'll get plenty of everything.

MR. CONNOLLY

You'd better not count on us . . .

MRS. CONNOLLY

Thank you anyway, Miss Miller.

The elevator door closes. Miss Miller crosses to the lobby door and goes out.

PASTRY SHOP

The only other customer is just paying for her purchases. The customer and the young girl clerk both look at Miss Miller who is hoarsely inhaling great breaths of air as if she has been running. By the time the other customer has been handed her boxes and leaves, Miss Miller's breathing is almost back to normal.

MISS MILLER

I'd like some . . . some vanilla eclairs, please.

CLERK

Yes, Ma'm. How many would you like?

MISS MILLER

Oh, let's see. Two, four . . . uh . . . if the Connollys come with their friends—that'll be eight more . . . if I serve two apiece—one dozen should be enough.

CLERK

Yes, Ma'm.

MISS MILLER

I don't think anybody would eat more than two, do you?

CLERK

(putting the eclairs into a pastry box)
Oh no, Ma'm.

MISS MILLER

Except my little friend, Miriam. She has a sweet
tooth. She may eat four all by herself.

CLERK

Would you like me to add a couple extra?

MISS MILLER

No. I'm not going to *permit* her to eat four. Then
she'll have a tummy ache and I'd have to nurse
her, won't I?

CLERK
(*smiling*)
They *are* awfully rich.

*Miss Miller hands the clerk two dollars and takes the pastry
box. The clerk turns to the cash register and rings up the money
as Miss Miller crosses to the door.*

MISS MILLER
(*to clerk*)
Thank you. I wonder . . . uh . . . would you mind
stepping out on the sidewalk and telling me if you
see a little dwarf on a platform attached to
roller skates?

CLERK
(*not sure she has heard correctly*)
Huh?

MISS MILLER

I think he's a beggar and he's persecuting me
because I won't buy his pencils.

The clerk shrugs and crosses to the show window to look out.

CLERK

I don't see any beggar.

MISS MILLER

Please go out on the sidewalk and look.

CLERK

I'm sorry, Ma'm. I can't leave the shop alone.
(*she peers out again*)
No one on roller skates . . . with pencils or
anything.

MISS MILLER
(*like a frightened child*)
Are you sure?

CLERK
Cross my heart.

Timidly, Miss Miller opens the door and leaves. The cripple is nowhere in sight and not hiding in the next doorway. Sure that he has gone at last, Miss Miller strides along with confidence. As she comes to the corner, she stops, gasps and turns pale. The little cripple on his platform is leaning against the building. When he sees her he lifts his cap, waves it jauntily in the air and gives her a great big obscene wink.

CUT TO:

MISS MILLER'S LIVING ROOM

We have a feeling that it is late at night. The sky is black outside the windows. The roses are in a vase on the coffee table. Next to them is a large plate on which are eight vanilla eclairs arranged in a semicircle—it must be quite evident that the four more needed to complete the circle are missing. Miss Miller is seated on the couch nibbling an eclair. The canary is hopping about in its cage.

MISS MILLER
(*to the canary*)
Guess she's not going to come, Tommy. What a pity, after all the trouble I went to, to get these eclairs. What an unreliable child she is.

She pops the last bite of eclair into her mouth and chews it up.

MISS MILLER
Well, we're just not going to wait any longer. That's all there is to it. She can ring and ring and ring. We're going to bed.

She crosses to get the cover for the canary's cage. On the way she staggers a bit and appears to feel faint.

MISS MILLER
I feel a little dizzy.

She reaches out to hold on to a chair to steady herself.

    MISS MILLER
Oh, I don't feel well at all . . . shouldn't have eaten
all those eclairs . . .
    (gets the cover and crosses to the cage with it)
It's all that child's fault. If she'd only come on
time . . .
    (starts to drape the cage)
You go straight to bed like a good boy. Your old
Nanny isn't feeling very well tonight and she
can't be jumping up to bother with you. Here comes
the sandman to sprinkle sand in your eyes!

*The cage is covered. She walks slowly across the hall and into
her bedroom. Suddenly she stops in amazement which immediately turns to fury. Miriam is sitting cross-legged on the floor, a
large leatherette jewel box in front of her, and is casually rummaging through it.*

    MIRIAM
    (looking up with her characteristic smile)
Hello!

    MISS MILLER
*How did you get in here? What are you doing
with my things?*

    MIRIAM
You don't have anything very good, do you?
    (she holds up several strings of beads)
These are just glass. Besides, I don't like the color.

She drops the beads back into the box.

    MISS MILLER
    (indignantly)
I have been waiting for you all evening long . . .

    MIRIAM
    (casually)
I know.
    (she tries a ring on her finger)
This isn't bad, but the stone is so tiny. Is it a
real ruby?

MISS MILLER

Put it down! You have no right to go through my
jewel case . . .

MIRIAM

It's not a jewel case . . . because you haven't any
jewels. It's a trinket box.

She picks out a pin and tosses it back.

MISS MILLER

Explain yourself to me immediately! *How did you
get in here?*
(*suddenly, suspiciously*)
When I was in the kitchen washing up the
supper dishes?

MIRIAM
(*picks up a pin*)
This is a pretty silver pin, but it needs polishing.

MISS MILLER

I must have left the door unlocked.

*Miriam holds up a small gold heart-shaped locket on a slender
gold chain.*

MIRIAM
(*her eyes sparkling*)
Oh my! This is beautiful!

MISS MILLER

Put that back. Put everything back where you
found it. And leave this apartment at once!

Miriam slips the chain over her head.

MISS MILLER

Did you hear what I said? *I want you to leave!*

MIRIAM
(*admiring the locket on her chest*)
Let me keep this. Please! Please give it to me!

*Miss Miller sways a bit and with a muffled groan slumps down
on the edge of her bed.*

MISS MILLER

Oh . . . I don't feel well. You must go now.

MIRIAM
I want this locket! Give it to me!

MISS MILLER
(*weakly*)
No. It was a present from my father—when I was
a little girl.

MIRIAM
(*coldly*)
You're old now. What do *you* need it for?

She runs to the dresser and stares at herself in the mirror.

MIRIAM
It's lovely on me. I'm going to keep it!

MISS MILLER
I can't bear you! All your naughty tricks! Taking
things that don't belong to you . . . appearing and
disappearing . . . I can't bear it.

MIRIAM
(*slyly*)
Would you like me to move in with you? We can
live here together and you'll always know where
I am.

MISS MILLER
(*almost a sob*)
Go away and leave me alone.
        (*she stretches out on the bed*)
I don't feel well. I'm sick.

MIRIAM
All right . . . but first I'm going to give you a big
kiss in exchange for the locket.

MISS MILLER
No, please don't . . .

Miriam leans over and kisses her exuberantly on the cheek.

MIRIAM
Good night, old Nanny!

She skips happily to the door and out of the bedroom.

> MISS MILLER
> (crying)
> I'm not your Nanny.

                                                        CUT TO:

INT.: *Miss Miller's LIVING ROOM. NIGHT*

The phone rings. Miss Miller, in nightgown and robe, her hair bedraggled, looking washed out and weakened, walks in with a thermometer in her mouth. She takes the thermometer out of her mouth and answers the phone.

> MISS MILLER
> (into phone)
> Hello. Mrs. Connolly! . . . How kind of you to
> call . . . No, nothing's wrong—I've been a bit ill for
> a couple of days—but it's over now . . .
> (she is examining the thermometer)
> I've just taken my temperature . . . normal . . .
> Oh, I do thank you, but I don't feel a bit hungry.
> I think I'll just make myself a cup of tea and I'll
> be tip-top by tomorrow. Absolutely. . . . I promise . . .
> of course. I'll let you know . . . Goodbye . . .

She hangs up and starts out of her bedroom, presumably to the kitchen. When she gets to the hallway, her doorbell rings. She stops, confused.

> MISS MILLER
> Who can that be?

The doorbell continues to ring insistently. Several long rings and then continuously as if someone is holding a finger down on it. Miss Miller hurries through the living room to the door.

> MISS MILLER
> Just a minute, just a minute . . . I'm coming.

At the door she looks through the peephole. Miriam is standing in the hallway holding a large package. She stares up at the peephole.

> MISS MILLER
> Go away.

> MIRIAM
> Hurry and open the door—this package is heavy.

> MISS MILLER
> Go away. I don't want you here.

> MIRIAM
> Oh please—I brought you such a nice present.

Miss Miller is silent.

> MIRIAM
> Don't you want to see the lovely surprise I've
> brought you?

> MISS MILLER
> *(after a moment she starts to unfasten the
> chain)*
> You'll have to go in a few minutes. I am not well.

She finally gets the door open.

> MIRIAM
> *(peevishly)*
> Really, you're such a slowpoke . . .
> *(she thrusts the package at her)*
> Here, take this. It's awfully heavy.

Reluctantly Miss Miller helps her carry the box inside. She closes the door. Miriam takes off her hat and coat. She is wearing the locket. She flings herself wearily into a chair. Her eye lights on the vase of white roses already a little wilted and losing their petals.

> MIRIAM
> The roses are dying . . .

> MISS MILLER
> They've been here for three days.

> MIRIAM
> That's how you know something's real, isn't it . . .
> because *real* things die.
> *(she gazes around)*
> By the way, where are the eclairs?

MISS MILLER
(*dully*)
Eclairs?

MIRIAM
Vanilla. You know, the ones you promised me.

MISS MILLER
Oh. I . . . I threw them all out.

MIRIAM
(*severely*)
You shouldn't have done that.
(*then, with a smile*)
But I'll forgive you. You can buy me some more
tomorrow.

She looks over at the bird cage, already draped for the night.

MIRIAM
I see Tommy is asleep.

MISS MILLER
Yes.

MIRIAM
Perhaps the sun will shine in the morning and then
I'll hear him sing.

MISS MILLER
Morning? Afraid you won't be here in the morning.
In fact, I think you'd better go right now.

MIRIAM
(*suddenly*)
Oh, you've forgotten about my box and the present
I brought you. Go on, open it.

*Against her will, as if some force outside of herself is making her
do it, Miss Miller kneels in front of the box and opens the flaps.
Lying on top is the umbrella Miriam took from the automat.
Miss Miller narrows her lips and frowns at Miriam. She lifts
the umbrella out of the box and puts it on the floor. On top of
the contents now there is a white silk dress similar to the one
Miriam always wears, folded neatly. Miss Miller stares at it.*

MIRIAM
Go on, see what else there is . . .

Miss Miller lifts out the dress and finds another identical one. She frowns and lifts it out too. Beneath it is another exactly like the first two. She plunges her hands along the inside edge of the box and we see that it is filled with identical white silk dresses. She stares at Miriam.

> MISS MILLER
> They're all yours!

> MIRIAM
> That's right.

> MISS MILLER
> Why did you bring them here?

> MIRIAM
> Because I've come to live with you . . .

> MISS MILLER
> *(rises, aghast)*
> But you can't! For God's sake, go away . . . go away
> and leave me alone!

> MIRIAM
> *(calmly)*
> I'm staying. I think I'll be happy here.

> MISS MILLER
> *(firmly and loudly)*
> I absolutely will not permit it. I don't want you
> in my house.

> MIRIAM
> If you look underneath all my dresses, you'll find
> the present I brought you.

> MISS MILLER
> *(beginning to panic; shouting)*
> I don't want any presents from you. Get out!
> Do you hear? Get out!

> MIRIAM
> Hush, for goodness sake. You'll wake the neighbors!
> *(wheedling)*
> Go on, look at your nice present!

Wordlessly Miss Miller shakes her head and backs away from Miriam. With an exasperated sigh the little girl runs to the box, digs down under all the dresses and triumphantly pulls out a doll. It is a limp, long-limbed doll—the kind that years ago was not used as a toy so much as a decorative object to be placed against the bolster of a bed. This one is dressed in an elaborate French costume of the Marie Antoinette period and wears an exquisite powdered wig. Clearly it is far from new and shows signs of a great deal of handling, but it is in good condition except that one of its glass eyes is missing. The other stares idiotically at Miss Miller as Miriam waves the doll at her in triumph.

Miss Miller's face dissolves into a mask of ugly red lines. She begins to cry, an unnatural tearless sort of weeping as though, not having wept for a long time, she has forgotten how. Carefully she edges backwards toward the apartment door. When she feels the knob behind her, she twists it with one swift motion, rushes out into the hall. She runs down the hall to the Connollys' door and knocks as hard as she can.

Mrs. Connolly opens the door. When she sees Miss Miller's condition, an expression of alarm crosses her face.

> MISS MILLER
> (*gasping*)
> Oh—Let me in . . . please . . .

Mrs. Connolly takes her arm, draws her inside and closes the door. The apartment is a duplicate of Miss Miller's. As they go into the living room, Miss Miller now weeping loudly, Mr. Connolly comes in from the kitchen with a drink in his hand.

> MRS. CONNOLLY
> (*to Miss Miller*)
> Miss Miller, what's wrong? What happened?
> (*consolingly to the sobbing woman*)
> Oh, you poor dear . . . tell us what we can do . . .

> MISS MILLER
> (*to both of them*)
> I'm so ashamed for behaving this way . . .
> (*she presses her hands over her face*)
> It sounds so ridiculous . . .

> MRS. CONNOLLY
> Tell us, honey—what's the trouble?

MISS MILLER
There's someone in my apartment . . .

MR. CONNOLLY
A prowler?

MISS MILLER
No, a little girl. I'm afraid of her.

MR. CONNOLLY
(*exchanging a glance with his wife*)
A little girl?

MISS MILLER
She won't leave—I can't make her. She's going to
do something terrible . . . I know she is. She has
already stolen my locket . . .

MR. CONNOLLY
Is she a relative or something?

MISS MILLER
No . . . I have no living relations. I don't know
who she is . . . or where she came from. But she's
going to do something terrible . . .

MRS. CONNOLLY
You've got to calm down, honey. George is going
to see about the kid . . .

MR. CONNOLLY
You want her out . . . I'll get her out.

MISS MILLER
I'm so ashamed to be making such a fuss . . .

MRS. CONNOLLY
(*soothing*)
Oh, we know. Kids today are such brats . . .

MR. CONNOLLY
Is the door open?

Miss Miller nods. He drains his drink and crosses to leave.

MR. CONNOLLY
(*to his wife*)
Maybe you should get her a stiff drink.

He leaves.

           MRS. CONNOLLY
Would you like a drink? To quiet your nerves?

           MISS MILLER
No, I never imbibe. All I want is to make that little
girl leave me alone.
           (she looks at Mrs. Connolly with bitter
           conviction)
But, I'm being tortured these days by all sorts of
people. The other day on the street a dwarf
followed me. He had a little platform with roller
skates and he chased me! And then you know what
he did? He *winked* at me! Why would a *dwarf*
wink at *me?*

Mrs. Connolly tries to camouflage an accelerating embarrassment
which Miss Miller abruptly detects.

           MISS MILLER
I'm not inventing it. I'm a very sane, down-to-earth
person. I'm speaking the truth!

           MRS. CONNOLLY
Of course you are, honey. I'm going to make you
a nice cup of tea.

She starts to rise.

           MISS MILLER
No, I don't want any tea. And then there was a
telephone call. Some stranger called me up and
asked me to meet him in a bar! Can you *imagine*
such a thing?

           MRS. CONNOLLY
           (lamely)
The city is full of nuts . . .

           MISS MILLER
And now this child . . . she moved right in with
my dresses and my dolls—everything!

Mrs. Connolly gives her a long appraising look.

MRS. CONNOLLY

You've been sick. Your nerves are on edge. George'll get rid of the girl and everything will be all right.

At this moment Mr. Connolly returns. He walks in frowning.

MR. CONNOLLY

There's nobody in the place. Looked all over.

MRS. CONNOLLY

Are you sure?

MR. CONNOLLY

Nobody there. Looked all over and there's nobody there.

MRS. CONNOLLY

Sure she's not in one of the closets?

MR. CONNOLLY

Nowhere. Nobody. Zero.

MISS MILLER

Did you see a box of dresses or a doll?

MR. CONNOLLY

No Ma'm. I didn't.

His eyes slide sideways to meet his wife's gaze. Miss Miller is quite aware of the exchange and of the shared suspicions of the Connollys. She rises, composing her face and firming her voice.

MISS MILLER

No doubt I've been very foolish.

She starts toward the door.

MRS. CONNOLLY

(*going with her*)
Let me go with you . . . just in case . . .

MISS MILLER

Forgive my disturbing you. I've already imposed on your kindness. Anyway, I've nothing to be afraid of now.

MRS. CONNOLLY

Well, honey . . . you just come right back if you need us.

She closes the door softly behind Miss Miller. Turns to her husband. They roll their eyes at each other.

HALL

Miss Miller crosses the hall from the Connollys'. She opens her own door and goes inside.

FOYER

She looks fearfully around the foyer and what she can see of the living room. The apartment is very quiet and does indeed seem empty. Miss Miller sighs with relief. Suddenly from the living room comes the sound of a canary singing. Miss Miller's eyes widen. She holds the wall for support. Then she walks slowly into the living room.

LIVING ROOM

It is empty. She approaches the cage still covered by its cloth. As suddenly as it began the bird stops singing. Miss Miller turns away from the cage and there sitting primly on the couch is Miriam. Miss Miller gasps and presses a hand to her mouth.

> MIRIAM
> *(with a small smile)*
> Hello!

> MISS MILLER
> *(sinking into a chair)*
> Mr. Connolly said you weren't here.

> MIRIAM
> *(with a giggle)*
> And you believed him? Well, he was wrong, wasn't he?

> MISS MILLER
> Where were you hiding, you bad girl?

> MIRIAM
> I wasn't hiding.

> MISS MILLER
> *(with a groan)*
> Oh, I can't stand it any more . . . all your lies.

MIRIAM
(*grimly*)
I never tell lies and you know it.

Their eyes meet.

MIRIAM
Don't you, Miriam?

MISS MILLER
Don't you dare call me by my first name. Apologize
immediately.

MIRIAM
Mrs. Connolly makes all sorts of excuses not to
accept your invitations. She doesn't want to accept
them. The Connollys think you're *boring*!

MISS MILLER
Oh, you wicked, wicked girl!

MIRIAM
Nina Whitfield Packard . . . she hasn't engaged a
nurse for her baby at all. She just doesn't want *you*!

MISS MILLER
Don't . . . don't . . . I don't want to hear any more.
Just go away, please go away.

MIRIAM
Running down to the mailbox four times a day
to look for a wedding invitation from Millicent
Castle! She hasn't *sent* you an invitation!

MISS MILLER
(*pleading*)
Yes, she has!

MIRIAM
Why hasn't it come? The wedding's tomorrow.

*Miss Miller presses her hands to her mouth. Her eyes stare
wildly at Miriam.*

MIRIAM
Everyone lies to you but me. You even lie to
yourself.

Miriam rises and crosses to the shelf of photographs. As she walks we hear the characteristic rustle of her dress. She picks up one of the photographs and slams it to the floor. The glass shatters into bits.

MIRIAM
Selfish little brat!

MISS MILLER
Huuhhh!

She leaps to her feet but stands there transfixed with horror.

MIRIAM
Nasty little snip!

MISS MILLER
Stop that!

MIRIAM
(she picks up another photograph)
Ungrateful little monsters . . . they've forgotten all about you.

MISS MILLER
Liar! Liar!

Miriam slams the second photo to the floor.

MIRIAM
You've hardly slept through a night because of them, cleaned up their messes, nursed them through fevers, wiped up their vomit, put up with their tantrums, you've given your life for them . . . they don't even know you're alive.

MISS MILLER
Liar! Liar! Liar! Give it to me! Give it to me! Liar! Liar! Liar! Liar!

She slams a third photograph to the floor and picks up another. Miss Miller hurls herself across the room and wrestles with Miriam, trying to get the photo away from her. The photo falls to their feet but they keep on wrestling, hitting at each other, tugging, grasping, kicking, no holds barred. Miss Miller is gradually dragging Miriam toward the wide open window. We hear

the sound of their grunts and gasps as they struggle and fight. Miss Miller gets Miriam up against the window and with what seems like some final superhuman effort pushes her up and backwards and out. She stands at the window sill shaking and drawing in huge shivering breaths for an instant. Then she slams the window shut.

Still breathing hard, she drags herself across the room, picks up the shattered photographs and lays them safely on the shelf. By this time she is crying, small whimpering cries of a wounded animal. She turns out the lamps in the living room and goes into her bedroom. Her bed is open just as she left it. She climbs into it, settles back on the pillows. She heaves one long final sigh and lies still staring at the ceiling. She closes her eyes. Suddenly and very softly we hear the rustling sound of silk. Miss Miller's eyes snap open. She blinks at the ceiling. We hear the rustling silk again. Slowly Miss Miller lets her chin drop to her chest so she can look toward the foot of the bed. There sits Miriam, cross-legged, her lips barely curled as she smiles her horrible little smile.

> MIRIAM
> Hello!

LONG, SLOW DISSOLVE TO Among the Paths to Eden

MISS MILLER
Mildred Natwick

MIRIAM
Susan Dunfee

MISS LAKE
Carol Gustafson

film credits

EMILY
Robin Ponterio

NINA
Beverly Ballard

MAN IN THEATER *Frederic Morton*   MRS. CONNOLLY *Jane Connell*
MAN IN AUTOMAT *Richard Hamilton*   MR. CONNOLLY *Brooks Rogers*
WOMAN IN AUTOMAT *Phyllis Eldridge* CLERK IN SHOP *Niki Flacks*
                                     DWARF *Tony Ross*

DIRECTOR/PRODUCER *Frank Perry*
SCREENPLAY *Truman Capote & Eleanor Perry*
MUSIC *Meyer Kupferman*
PHOTOGRAPHY *Joseph Brun, A.S.C.*
PRODUCTION DESIGNER *Peter Dohanos*
FILM EDITOR *Patricia Jaffe*
IN CHARGE OF PRODUCTION *Joel Glickman*
ASSISTANT TO MR. PERRY *Lynn Forman*
COSTUME DESIGNER *Frank Thompson*
RECORDING SUPERVISOR *Dick Vorisek*
ASSISTANT DIRECTORS *Stanley Ackerman & George Goodman*
WARDROBE *Marilyn Putnam*
SCRIPT SUPERVISOR *Kay Chapin*
SET DECORATOR *Leif Pedersen*
SOUND *Chuck Federmack & Nat Boxer*
CAMERA OPERATOR *Peter Garbarini*

Miriam is scheduled for televising by the American Broadcasting Company in the spring of 1970. It was scheduled to receive its world premiere as a motion picture (together with *A Christmas Memory* and *Among the Paths to Eden*) as *Trilogy,* the official American entry at the 1968 Cannes Film Festival.

THE KEY to this adaptation lies in the character of Mrs. Miller. All we know about her from the story is that she is a widow and a recluse. Once we fill in the details of her life we'll have some clues as to why she is slipping into a schizophrenic breakdown and why her delusions take the form of the child, Miriam.

Mrs. Miller becomes a spinster and a nanny

Possibly Mrs. Miller could equally well have been a saleslady, or a waitress, or a typist, but in that case it might have been more difficult to justify the delusion of Miriam. Why not a phantom lover or a parent figure? Why not a totally different way of losing hold of reality?

If we made Mrs. Miller an unmarried woman who has spent decades of her life taking care of other people's children, it seemed natural that she would conjure up a child companion in the depths of her loneliness.

Miss Miller's biography

Once she became a nanny dozens of ideas about her and her life came to mind. This is a woman who has had no real personal life, none of the normal satisfactions of being a wife and a mother. She has always lived in rooms in other people's houses, tolerated on the periphery of other people's lives— not a member of the family, not quite a servant. She would probably describe her own background as "genteel"—we felt it was rigid and cold, without affection or *joie de vivre*. Miss Miller's social insecurity makes her a snob, her limited education makes her suspicious of anything unfamiliar. She is compulsive about good manners and the other rituals of what she would call "breeding."

We felt, too, that Miss Miller wasn't a particularly talented baby nurse, that she had little psychological understanding of children and not much intuitive maternal feeling. On the other hand she was a decent, kindly, dependable woman who took good physical care of her charges.

why the breakdown?

Miss Miller is bitterly lonely. Wherever she turns she is rejected—by a strange nurse she meets in the park, by a young mother she formerly nursed, by strangers in the automat, by the neighbors in her apartment. (This last was accentuated in the TV version by a scene showing Miss Miller trying to get the neighbors to come to a movie with her and their transparent excuses. She then goes to the movies alone and meets Miriam.)

No matter how eagerly she reaches out to other people she is continually rebuffed. The only relationship she seems to have is with a canary. Before our film play begins she has been slowly losing her hold on reality. Perhaps she behaved in eccentric ways, talked out loud to herself, etc. The last and most shattering blow she receives is from the young pregnant woman who refuses to hire her as nurse for the coming baby. Probably

the hope of this job was all that was holding Miss Miller together. Once that hope is gone, she breaks down. Her delusions start as a kind of pleasant, playful daydream of Miriam and increase in horror to become demented nightmares.

who is Miriam?

Without becoming too clinical or attempting to dramatize a psychiatric case history, our rationale for the character of Miriam was that she stood for the submerged part of Miss Miller. Physically she is Miss Miller as a child. Psychically she is what Miss Miller really thinks and feels under the smothering layers of inhibition and hypocrisy with which she armors herself. This armor has served as her defense against the truth. Once it begins to crack, the real Miss Miller (Miriam) surfaces in front of our eyes. The lies that she has lived by for so long begin to retreat as Miriam utters the devastating truths.

theme

Despite the fact that Miss Miller has worked hard all her life and has been useful to many people she is now, as she ages and her capacities fade, cast off by society. She is no longer needed. She is a leftover about whom nobody cares. She is, in effect, set apart on an emotional ice block without human warmth or contact. This is the major idea which emerged in the film play. Even though Miss Miller has become a rather boring, pathetic, eccentric woman, she is still a human being, vulnerable and wounded, and as such cannot simply be used and thrown away.

clues

In a sense Miriam is a mystery story, the mystery revolving around the identity of the little girl.

In the opening scene of the TV version Miss Miller offers peppermints to the child in the park. Later when we see Miriam for the first time she is eating peppermints, and again in the automat. This visual clue no longer works because so much of the opening scene had to be cut. However we do use the coincidence of the names from the story and add the coincidence of the hair-color. This may seem to be a total giveaway but since it occurs so early in the film the audiences apparently don't leap to any conclusions.

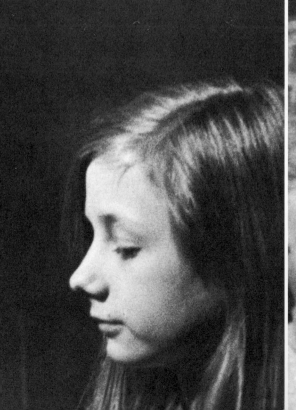

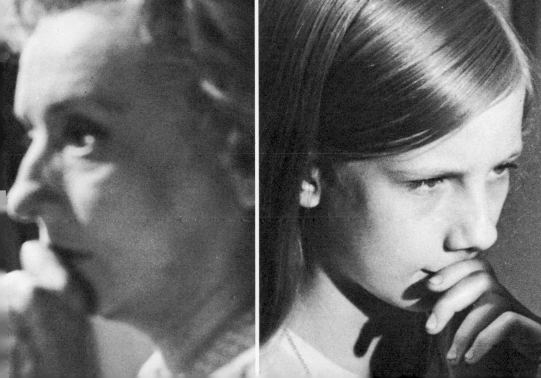

Later Miriam says, "You don't like imitations *either* . . ." (page 80) and still later we see Miss Miller eating the vanilla eclairs of which Miriam is so fond. Finally, in the penultimate scene, where Miss Miller has gone to seek help from the neighbors, she makes a slip of the tongue: "And now this child! She moved in with my dresses and my dolls. . . ."

the little beggar

He was invented during a discussion about the old man in the story (page 54). Clearly this is the old man Miriam refers to when she says to Mrs. Miller "The last place I lived was with an old man. . . ." (Perhaps Miriam represents everyone's delusions. Or is she the Angel of Death?) We changed the old man into the little dwarf on the rolling platform partly for the sake of movement and menace. (In the TV version he follows Miss Miller for several blocks, the noise of the roller skate wheels under his platform becomes more and more threatening.)

The beggar is not a delusion. He is meant to be real. So is the anonymous telephone call near the beginning of the film. These are simply two things that could happen to anyone in a big city. To a normal person they might cause a brief annoyance. To a person whose sanity is as fragile as Miss Miller's, they are immensely frightening.

the ending

The tensions and the conflicts have certainly
been heightened in the filmplay and the emotional
"colors" in the script are far more violent than
in the story. Of the three stories this is the one we
"adapted" most—that is, departed from, embroidered
on, felt the freest with. We felt, however,
that we had not violated the dramatic laws of
cause and effect and that Miss Miller in her rage
and fear of the truth would indeed try to kill
Miriam. Unless Miriam can be made to vanish,
Miss Miller is aware that there will be nothing left
except her total immersion in schizophrenia.
In our filmplay end she becomes, we think,
admirable in her tenacious urge to survive.

Among the Paths to Eden

the story

One Saturday in March, an occasion of pleasant winds and sailing clouds, Mr. Ivor Belli bought from a Brooklyn florist a fine mass of jonquils and conveyed them, first by subway, then foot, to an immense cemetery in Queens, a site unvisited by him since he had seen his wife buried there the previous autumn. Sentiment could not be credited with returning him today, for Mrs. Belli, to whom he had been married twenty-seven years, during which time she had produced two now-grown and matrimonially settled daughters, had been a woman of many natures, most of them trying: he had no desire to renew so unsoothing an acquaintance, even in spirit. No; but a hard winter had just passed, and he felt in need of exercise, air, a heart-lifting stroll through the handsome, spring-prophesying weather; of course, rather as an extra dividend, it was nice that he would be able to tell his daughters of a journey to their mother's grave, especially so since it might a little appease the elder girl, who seemed resentful of Mr. Belli's too comfortable acceptance of life as lived alone.

The cemetery was not a reposeful, pretty place; was, in fact, a damned frightening one: acres of fog-colored stone spilled across a sparsely grassed and shadeless plateau. An unhindered view of Manhattan's skyline provided the location with beauty of a stage-prop sort—it loomed beyond the graves like a steep headstone honoring these quiet folk, its used up and very former citizens: the juxtaposed spectacle made Mr. Belli, who was by profession a tax accountant and therefore equipped to enjoy irony however sadistic, smile, actually chuckle—yet, oh God in heaven, its inferences chilled him, too, deflated the buoyant stride carrying him along the cemetery's rigid, pebbled paths. He slowed until he stopped, thinking: "I ought to have taken Morty to the zoo"; Morty being his grandson, aged three. But it would be churlish not to continue, vengeful: and why waste a bouquet? The combination of thrift and virtue reactivated him; he was breathing hard from hurry when, at last, he stooped to jam the jonquils into a rock urn perched on a rough gray slab engraved with Gothic calligraphy declaring that

SARAH BELLI
1901–1959

had been the

DEVOTED WIFE OF IVOR
BELOVED MOTHER OF IVY AND REBECCA.

Lord, what a relief to know the woman's tongue was finally stilled. But the thought, pacifying as it was, and though supported by visions of his new and silent bachelor's apartment, did not relight the suddenly snuffed-out sense of immortality, of glad-to-be-aliveness, which the day had earlier kindled. He had set forth expecting such good from the air, the walk, the aroma of another spring about to be. Now he wished he had worn a scarf; the sunshine was false, without real warmth, and the wind, it seemed to him, had grown rather wild. As he gave the jonquils a decorative pruning, he regretted he could not delay their doom by supplying them with water; relinquishing the flowers, he turned to leave.

A woman stood in his way. Though there were few other visitors to the cemetery, he had not noticed her before, or heard her approach. She did not step aside. She glanced at the jonquils; presently her eyes, situated behind steel-rimmed glasses, swerved back to Mr. Belli.

"Uh. Relative?"

"My wife," he said, and sighed as though some such noise was obligatory.

She sighed, too; a curious sigh that implied gratification. "Gee, I'm sorry."

Mr. Belli's face lengthened. "Well."

"It's a shame."

"Yes."

"I hope it wasn't a long illness. Anything painful."

"No-o-o," he said, shifting from one foot to the other. "In her sleep." Sensing an unsatisfied silence, he added, "Heart condition."

"Gee. That's how I lost my father. Just recently. Kind of gives us something in common. Something," she said, in a tone alarmingly plaintive, "something to talk about."

"—know how you must feel."

"At least they didn't suffer. That's a comfort."

The fuse attached to Mr. Belli's patience shortened. Until now he had kept his gaze appropriately lowered, observing, after his initial glimpse of her, merely the woman's shoes, which were of the sturdy, so-called sensible type often worn by aged women and nurses. "A great comfort," he said, as he executed three tasks: raised his eyes, tipped his hat, took a step forward.

Again the woman held her ground; it was as though she had been employed to detain him. "Could you give me the time? My old clock," she announced, self-consciously tapping some dainty machinery strapped to her wrist, "I got it for graduating high school. That's why it doesn't run so good any more. I mean, it's pretty old. But it makes a nice appearance."

Mr. Belli was obliged to unbutton his topcoat and plow around for a gold watch embedded in a vest pocket. Meanwhile, he scrutinized the lady, really took her apart. She must have been blond as a child, her general coloring suggested so: the clean shine of her Scandinavian skin, her chunky cheeks, flushed with peasant health, and the blueness of her genial eyes —such honest eyes, attractive despite the thin silver spectacles surrounding them; but the hair itself, what could be discerned of it under a drab felt hat, was poorly permanented frizzle of no particular tint. She was a bit taller than Mr. Belli, who was five-foot-eight with the aid of shoe lifts, and she may have weighed more; at any rate he couldn't imagine that she mounted scales too cheerfully. Her hands: kitchen hands; and the nails: not only nibbled ragged, but painted with a pearly lacquer queerly phosphorescent. She wore a plain brown coat and carried a plain black purse. When the student of these components recomposed them he found they assembled themselves into a very decent-looking person whose looks he liked; the nail polish was discouraging; still he felt that here was someone you could trust. As he trusted Esther Jackson, Miss Jackson, his secretary. Indeed, that was who she reminded him of, Miss Jackson; not that the comparison was fair—to Miss Jackson, who possessed, as he had once in the course of a quarrel informed Mrs. Belli, "intellectual elegance and elegance otherwise." Nevertheless, the woman confronting him seemed imbued with that quality of goodwill he appreciated in his secretary, Miss Jackson, Esther (as he'd lately, absent-mindedly, called her). Moreover, he guessed them to be about the same age: rather on the right side of forty.

"Noon. Exactly."

"Think of that! Why, you must be famished," she said, and unclasped her purse, peered into it as though it were a picnic hamper crammed with sufficient treats to furnish a smörgåsbord. She scooped out a fistful of peanuts. "I practically live on peanuts since Pop—since I haven't anyone to cook for. I must say, even if I do say so, I miss my own cooking; Pop always said I was better than any restaurant he ever went to. But it's no pleasure cooking just for yourself, even when you *can* make pastries light as a leaf. Go on. Have some. They're fresh-roasted."

Mr. Belli accepted; he'd always been childish about peanuts and, as he sat down on his wife's grave to eat them, only hoped his friend had more. A gesture of his hand suggested that she sit beside him; he was surprised to see that the invitation seemed to embarrass her; sudden additions of pink saturated her cheeks, as though he'd asked her to transform Mrs. Belli's bier into a love bed.

"It's okay for you. A relative. But me. Would she like a stranger sitting on her—resting place?"

"Please. Be a guest. Sarah won't mind," he told her, grateful the dead cannot hear, for it both awed and amused him to consider what Sarah, that vivacious scene-maker, that energetic searcher for lipstick traces and stray blond strands, would say if she could see him shelling peanuts on her tomb with a woman not entirely unattractive.

And then, as she assumed a prim perch on the rim of the grave, he noticed her leg. Her left leg; it stuck straight out like a stiff piece of mischief with which she planned to trip passers-by. Aware of his interest, she smiled, lifted the leg up and down. "An accident. You know. When I was a kid. I fell off a roller coaster at Coney. Honest. It was in the paper. Nobody knows why I'm alive. The only thing is I can't bend my knee. Otherwise it doesn't make any difference. Except to go dancing. Are you much of a dancer?"

Mr. Belli shook his head; his mouth was full of peanuts.

"So that's something else we have in common. Dancing. I *might* like it. But I don't. I like music, though."

Mr. Belli nodded his agreement.

"And flowers," she added, touching the bouquet of jonquils; then her fingers traveled on and, as though she were reading Braille, brushed across the marble lettering on his name. "Ivor," she said, mispronouncing it. "Ivor Belli. My name is Mary O'Meaghan. But I wish *I* were Italian. My sister is; well, she married one. And oh, he's full of fun; happy-natured and outgoing, like all Italians. He says my spaghetti's the best he's ever had. Especially the kind I make with sea-food sauce. You ought to taste it."

Mr. Belli, having finished the peanuts, swept the hulls off his lap. "You've got a customer. But he's not Italian. Belli sounds like that. Only I'm Jewish."

She frowned, not with disapproval, but as if he had mysteriously daunted her.

"My family came from Russia; I was born there."

This last information restored her enthusiasm, accelerated it. "I don't care what they say in the papers. I'm sure Russians are the same as everybody else. Human. Did you see the Bolshoi Ballet on TV? Now didn't that make you proud to be a Russian?"

He thought: she means well; and was silent.

"Red cabbage soup—hot or cold—with sour cream. Hmnn. See," she said, producing a second helping of peanuts, "you *were* hungry. Poor fellow." She sighed. "How you must miss your wife's cooking."

It was true, he did; and the conversational pressure being applied to his appetite made him realize it. Sarah had set an excellent table: varied, on time, and well flavored. He recalled certain cinnamon-scented feastdays. Afternoons of gravy and wine, starchy linen, the "good" silver; followed by a nap. Moreover, Sarah had never asked him to dry a dish (he could hear her calmly humming in the kitchen), had never complained of housework; and she had contrived to make the raising of two girls a smooth series of thought-out, affectionate events; Mr. Belli's contribution to their upbringing had been to be an admiring witness; if his daughters were a credit to him (Ivy living in Bronxville, and married to a dental surgeon; her sister the wife of A. J. Krakower, junior partner in the law firm of Finnegan, Loeb and Krakower), he had Sarah to thank; they were her accomplishment. There was much to be said for Sarah, and he was glad to discover himself thinking so, to find himself remembering not the long hell of hours she had spent honing her tongue on his habits, supposed poker-playing, woman-chasing vices, but gentler episodes: Sarah showing off her self-made hats, Sarah scattering crumbs on snowy window sills for winter pigeons: a tide of visions that towed to sea the junk of harsher recollections. He felt, was all at once happy to feel, mournful, sorry he had not been sorry sooner; but, though he did genuinely value Sarah suddenly, he could not pretend regret that their life together had terminated, for the current arrangement was, on the whole, preferable by far. However, he wished that, instead of jonquils, he had brought her an orchid, the gala sort she'd always salvaged from her daughters' dates and stored in the icebox until they shriveled.

"—aren't they?" he heard, and wondered who had spoken until, blinking, he recognized Mary O'Meaghan, whose voice had been playing along unlistened to: a shy and lulling voice, a sound strangely small and young to come from so robust a figure.

"I said they must be cute, aren't they?"

"Well," was Mr. Belli's safe reply.

"Be modest. But I'm sure they are. If they favor their father; ha ha, don't take me serious, I'm joking. But, seriously, kids just slay me. I'll trade any kid for any grownup that ever lived. My sister has five, four boys and a girl. Dot, that's my sister, she's always after me to baby-sit now that I've got the time and don't have to look after Pop every minute. She and Frank, he's my brother-in-law, the one I mentioned, they say Mary, nobody can handle kids like *you*. At the same time have fun. But it's so easy; there's nothing like hot cocoa and a mean pillow fight to make kids sleepy. Ivy," she said, reading aloud the tombstone's dour script. "Ivy and Rebecca. Sweet names. And I'm sure you do your best. But two little girls without a mother."

"No, no," said Mr. Belli, at last caught up. "Ivy's a mother herself. And Becky's expecting."

Her face restyled momentary chagrin into an expression of disbelief. "A grandfather? You?"

Mr. Belli had several vanities: for example, he thought he was *saner* than other people; also, he believed himself to be a walking compass; his digestion, and an ability to read upside down, were other ego-enlarging items. But his reflection in a mirror aroused little inner applause; not that he disliked his appearance; he just knew that it was very so-what. The harvesting of his hair had begun decades ago; now his head was an almost barren field. While his nose had character, his chin, though it made a double effort, had none. His shoulders were broad; but so was the rest of him. Of course he was neat: kept his shoes shined, his laundry laundered, twice a day scraped and talcumed his bluish jowls; but such measures failed to camouflage, actually they emphasized, his middle-class, middle-aged ordinariness. Nonetheless, he did not dismiss Mary O'Meaghan's flattery; after all, an undeserved compliment is often the most potent.

"Hell, I'm fifty-one," he said, subtracting four years. "Can't say I feel it." And he didn't; perhaps it was because the wind had subsided, the warmth of the sun grown more authentic. Whatever the reason, his expectations had re-ignited, he was again immortal, a man planning ahead.

"Fifty-one. That's nothing. The prime. Is if you take care of yourself. A man your age needs tending to. Watching after."

Surely in a cemetery one was safe from husband stalkers? The question, crossing his mind, paused midway while he examined her cozy and gullible face, tested her gaze for guile. Though reassured, he thought it best to remind her of their surroundings. "Your father. Is he"—Mr. Belli gestured awkwardly—"nearby?"

"Pop? Oh, no. He was very firm; absolutely refused to be buried. So he's at home." A disquieting image gathered in Mr. Belli's head, one that her next words, "His ashes are," did not fully dispel. "Well," she shrugged, "that's how he wanted it. Oh—I see—you wondered why I'm here? I don't live too far away. It's somewhere to walk, and the view . . ." They both turned to stare at the skyline where the steeples of certain buildings flew pennants of cloud, and sun-dazzled windows glittered like a million bits of mica. Mary O'Meaghan said, "What a perfect day for a parade!"

Mr. Belli thought, *You're a very nice girl*; then he said it, too, and wished he hadn't, for naturally she asked him why. "Because. Well, that was nice what you said. About parades."

"See? So many things in common! I never miss a parade," she told him triumphantly. "The bugles. I play the bugle myself; used to, when I was at Sacred Heart. You said before—" She lowered her voice, as though approaching a subject that required grave tones. "You indicated you were a music lover. Because I have thousands of old records. Hundreds. Pop was in the business and that was his job. Till he retired. Shellacking records in a record factory. Remember Helen Morgan? She slays me, she really knocks me out."

"*Jesus* Christ," he whispered. Ruby Keeler, Jean Harlow: those had been keen but curable infatuations; but Helen Morgan, albino-pale, a sequinned wraith shimmering beyond Ziegfeld footlights—truly, truly he had loved her.

"Do you believe it? That she drank herself to death? On account of a gangster?"

"It doesn't matter. She was lovely."

"Sometimes, like when I'm alone and sort of fed up, I pretend I'm her. Pretend I'm singing in a night club. It's fun; you know?"

"Yes, I know," said Mr. Belli, whose own favorite fantasy was to imagine the adventures he might have if he were invisible.

"May I ask: would you do me a favor?"

"If I can. Certainly."

She inhaled, held her breath as if she were swimming under a wave of shyness; surfacing, she said: "Would you listen to my imitation? And tell me your honest opinion?" Then she removed her glasses: the silver rims had bitten so deeply their shape was permanently printed on her face. Her eyes, nude and moist and helpless, seemed stunned by freedom; the skimpily lashed lids fluttered like long-captive birds abruptly let loose. "There: everything's soft and smoky. Now you've got to use your imagination. So pretend I'm sitting on a piano—gosh, for-*give* me, Mr. Belli."

"Forget it. Okay. You're sitting on a piano."

"I'm sitting on a piano," she said, dreamily drooping her head backward until it assumed a romantic posture. She sucked in her cheeks, parted her lips; at the same moment Mr. Belli bit into his. For it was a tactless visit that glamour made on Mary O'Meaghan's filled-out and rosy face; a visit that should not have been paid at all; it was the wrong address. She waited, as though listening for music to cue her; then, *"Don't ever leave me, now that you're here! Here is where you belong. Everything seems so right when you're near, When you're away it's all wrong."* and Mr. Belli was shocked, for what he was hearing was exactly Helen Morgan's voice, and the voice, with its vulnerable sweetness, refinement, its tender quaver toppling high notes, seemed not to be borrowed, but Mary O'Meaghan's own, a natural expression of some secluded identity. Gradually she abandoned theatrical poses, sat upright singing with her eyes squeezed shut: *"—I'm so dependent, When I need comfort, I always run to you. Don't ever leave me! 'Cause if you do, I'll have no one to run to."* Until too late, neither she nor Mr. Belli noticed the coffin-laden entourage invading their privacy: a black caterpillar composed of sedate Negroes who stared at the white couple as though they had stumbled upon a pair of drunken grave robbers —except one mourner, a dry-eyed little girl who started laughing and couldn't stop; her hiccup-like hilarity resounded long after the procession had disappeared around a distant corner.

"If that kid was mine," said Mr. Belli.

"I feel so ashamed."

"Say, listen. What for? That was beautiful. I mean it; you can sing."

"Thanks," she said; and, as though setting up a barricade against impending tears, clamped on her spectacles.

"Believe me, I was touched. What I'd like is, I'd like an encore."

It was as if she were a child to whom he'd handed a balloon, a unique balloon that kept swelling until it swept her upward, danced her along with just her toes now and then touching ground. She descended to say: "Only not here. Maybe," she began, and once more seemed to be lifted, lilted through the air, "maybe sometime you'll let me cook you dinner. I'll plan it really Russian. And we can play records."

The thought, the apparitional suspicion that had previously passed on tiptoe, returned with a heavier tread, a creature fat and foursquare that Mr. Belli could not evict. "Thank you, Miss O'Meaghan. That's something to look forward to," he said. Rising, he reset his hat, adjusted his coat. "Sitting on cold stone too long, you can catch something."

"When?"

"Why, never. You should *never* sit on cold stone."

"When will you come to dinner?"

Mr. Belli's livelihood rather depended upon his being a skilled inventor of excuses. "Any time," he answered smoothly. "Except any time soon. I'm a tax man; you know what happens to us fellows in March. Yes sir," he said, again hoisting out his watch, "back to the grind for me." Still he couldn't—could he? —simply saunter off, leave her sitting on Sarah's grave? He owed her courtesy; for the peanuts, if nothing more, though there was more—perhaps it was due to her that he had remembered Sarah's orchids withering in the icebox. And anyway, she *was* nice, as likeable a woman, stranger, as he'd ever met. He thought to take advantage of the weather, but the weather offered none: clouds were fewer, the sun exceedingly visible. "Turned chilly," he observed, rubbing his hands together. "Could be going to rain."

"Mr. Belli. Now I'm going to ask you a very personal question," she said, enunciating each word decisively. "Because I wouldn't want you to think I go about inviting just anybody to dinner. My intentions are—" her eyes wandered, her voice wavered, as though the forthright manner had been a masquerade she could not sustain. "So I'm going to ask you a very personal question. Have you considered marrying again?"

He hummed, like a radio warming up before it speaks; when he did, it amounted to static: "Oh, at *my* age. Don't even want a dog. Just give me TV. Some beer. Poker once a week. Hell. Who the hell would want me?" he said; and, with a twinge, remembered Rebecca's mother-in-law, Mrs. A. J. Krakower, Sr., Dr. Pauline Krakower, a female dentist (retired) who had been an audacious participant in a certain family plot. Or what about Sarah's best friend, the persistent "Brownie" Pollock? Odd, but as long as Sarah lived he had enjoyed, upon occasion taken advantage of, "Brownie's" admiration; afterwards —finally he had *told* her not to telephone him any more (and she had shouted: "Everything Sarah ever said, she was right. You fat little *hairy* little bastard"). Then; and then there was Miss Jackson. Despite Sarah's suspicions, her in fact devout conviction, nothing untoward, very untoward, had transpired between him and the pleasant Esther, whose hobby was bowling. But he had always surmised, and in recent months known, that if one day he suggested drinks, dinner, a workout in some bowling alley . . . He said: "I *was* married. For twenty-seven years. That's enough for any lifetime"; but as he said it, he realized that, in just this moment, he had come to a decision, which was: he *would* ask Esther to dinner, he would take her bowling and buy her an orchid, a gala purple one with a lavender-ribbon bow. And where, he wondered, do couples honeymoon in April? At the latest May. Miami? Bermuda? Bermuda! "No, I've never considered it. Marrying again."

One would have assumed from her attentive posture that Mary O'Meaghan was raptly listening to Mr. Belli—except that her eyes played hookey, roamed as though she were hunting at a party for a different, more promising face. The color had drained from her own face; and with it had gone most of her healthy charm. She coughed.

He coughed. Raising his hat, he said: "It's been very pleasant meeting you, Miss O'Meaghan."

"Same here," she said, and stood up. "Mind if I walk with you to the gate?"

He did, yes; for he wanted to mosey along alone, devouring the tart nourishment of this spring-shiny, parade-weather, be alone with his many thoughts of Esther, his hopeful, zestful, live-forever mood. "A pleasure," he said, adjusting his stride to her slower pace and the slight lurch her stiff leg caused.

"But it *did* seem like a sensible idea," she said argumentatively. "And there was old Annie Austin: the living proof. Well, nobody had a *better* idea. I mean, everybody was at me: Get married. From the day Pop died, my sister and everybody was saying: Poor Mary, what's to become of her? A girl that can't type. Take shorthand. With her leg and all; can't even wait on table. What happens to a girl—a *grown* woman—that doesn't know anything, never done anything? Except cook and look after her father. All I heard was: Mary, you've got to get married."

"So. Why fight that? A fine person like you, you ought to be married. You'd make some fellow very happy."

"Sure I would. But *who?*" She flung out her arms, extended a hand toward Manhattan, the country, the continents beyond. "So I've looked; I'm not lazy by nature. But honestly, frankly, how does anybody ever find a husband? If they're not very, very pretty; a terrific dancer. If they're just—oh ordinary. Like me."

"No, no, not at all," Mr. Belli mumbled. "Not ordinary, no. Couldn't you make something of your talent? Your voice?"

She stopped, stood clasping and unclasping her purse. "Don't poke fun. Please. My life is at stake." And she insisted: "I *am* ordinary. So is old Annie Austin. And she says the place for me to find a husband—a decent, comfortable man—is in the obituary column."

For a man who believed himself a human compass, Mr. Belli had the anxious experience of feeling he had lost his way; with relief he saw the gates of the cemetery a hundred yards ahead. "She does? She says that? Old Annie Austin?"

"Yes. And she's a very practical woman. She feeds six people on $58.75 a week: food, clothes, everything. And the way she explained it, it certainly *sounded* logical. Because the obituaries are full of unmarried men. Widowers. You just go to the funeral and sort of introduce yourself: sympathize. Or the cemetery: come here on a nice day, or go to Woodlawn, there are always widowers walking around. Fellows thinking how much they miss home life and maybe wishing they were married again."

When Mr. Belli understood that she was in earnest, he was appalled; but he was also entertained: and he laughed, jammed his hands in his pockets and threw back his head. She joined him, spilled a laughter that restored her color, that, in skylarking style, made her rock against him. "Even I—" she said, clutching at his arm, "even *I* can see the humor." But it was not a lengthy vision; suddenly solemn, she said: "But that is how Annie met her husbands. Both of them: Mr. Cruikshank, and then Mr. Austin. So it *must* be a practical idea. Don't you think?"

"Oh, I do think."

She shrugged. "But it hasn't worked out too well. Us, for instance. *We* seemed to have such a lot in common."

"One day," he said, quickening his steps. "With a livelier fellow."

"I don't know. I've met some grand people. But it always ends like this. Like us . . ." she said, and left unsaid something more, for a new pilgrim, just entering through the gates of the cemetery, had attached her interest: an alive little man spouting cheery whistlings and with plenty of snap to his walk. Mr. Belli noticed him, too, observed the black band sewn round the sleeve of the visitor's bright green tweed coat, and commented: "Good luck, Miss O'Meaghan. Thanks for the peanuts."

Among the

ROSE
BELLI
1914-1966
DEVOTED WIFE
OF

Paths to Eden

the script

RESIDENTIAL CITY STREET

A row of houses, fairly substantial but old, most of them in need of paint. They have seen much better days and probably their early occupants were more prosperous than the ones who live there now. However the small front lawns are tidily kept.

She, wearing a coat and hat, comes out of one of the houses and down the steps to the sidewalk. It is a sunny breezy day in early spring. She wears a brown coat, neat but far from new, and a nondescript felt hat. Her shoes are what is known as "sensible" and she is carrying a capacious black handbag. She is about forty and must have been quite pretty as a young girl. Her features are pleasant, her skin still has a shine and her eyes are large and warm, ringed with dark lashes.

She turns up the sidewalk and starts off as if she has a destination firmly in mind. We notice that she has a very slight limp.

CITY STREET—BUSINESS SECTION

He emerges from a large office building and walks towards a subway entrance. He is a middle-aged man of quite ordinary appearance, obviously a nice man but with a soft disappointed expression. He wears a neat gray coat and felt hat. He strides along the street enjoying the spring weather.

At the entrance to the subway he comes to a flower stall. He stops and examines the flowers. Finally he takes a bunch of yellow jonquils out of its container and holds it out. The flower seller wraps them in tissue. He pays for them and continues down into the subway.

BRIDGE

She is striding across the bridge which provides pedestrians a safe way over the several traffic-loaded highways below. In the background we see a vast cemetery. In the distance is Manhattan, the skyscrapers lined up irregularly against the sky almost duplicate the outlines of the tombstones.

CEMETERY

He is walking briskly along carrying the bunch of jonquils. He stops at a neat enclosure of a double grave site. The sparse grass is just beginning to recover from winter and shows a few blades of green. At one end of the grave is a double tombstone. One side of it is blank. The other reads:

ROSE BELLI
1907–1966
BELOVED WIFE OF IVOR
BELOVED MOTHER OF IVY AND CARLA
ALWAYS IN OUR HEARTS

A rusted metal container of flowers, empty now, has toppled over at the bottom of the lettered half of the tombstone. He crosses to it, puts his flowers down on the grave and straightens the container. He unwraps his flowers and starts to arrange them in the container. He doesn't see her as she approaches quite near and stands behind him watching.

      SHE
      (after a moment)
   My, they're pretty!

He turns.

SHE
The flowers. I'm very partial to jonquils myself.

HE
They had white ones, but I thought that . . .

SHE
Oh, you were absolutely right.

He has turned back to fuss with his arrangement.

SHE
That looks very nice indeed.
(*cocks her head critically*)
Maybe if the stems weren't all the same length.
Maybe if the ones in front were a little shorter. . . .

HE
I see what you mean.

He takes a flower out of the holder and is about to break off the stem.

SHE
Oh no, no, no! Don't do that! Here.

She opens her bag and takes out a manicure scissors.

HE
Thank you.

He starts to cut off a few of the stems.

SHE
(*indicating the grave*)
Uh. Relative?

HE
Wife.

SHE
Gee, I'm sorry.

HE
(*with a long face*)
Well . . .

SHE
I hope it wasn't a long illness . . . anything
painful . . .

HE
No. In her sleep. Heart condition.

SHE
That's how I lost my father.

HE
I'm sorry . . .

SHE
At least they didn't suffer. That's some comfort.

He has finished shortening the flowers and rearranges them again.

SHE
Now that's going to look much better.
     (*he gives the flowers a final poke*)
Wonder how long they'll last. Too bad even
flowers have to . . . pass on, isn't it?
     (*he nods*)
What makes things precious is when you know
they have to . . . to pass on. That's how I felt about
my Pop. My sisters only came to see him once a
month but I was with him all the time. You only
have one father in this life and he's not going to be
with you forever. I expect you felt the same way about
your wife.

HE
Yes . . .

SHE
Of course a wife isn't the same as a parent. I mean
a man *can* have more than one wife . . . without
being at all disloyal.

HE
That's true.

SHE
     (*stares at the gravestone, then sympathetically*)
You just lost her last year—

HE
October.

SHE

If you married again nobody in the world would
criticize you. They say when a widower marries
again it's a real compliment to the first wife.

HE

I've heard that.

SHE

You losing your wife and me losing my father—
gives us something to talk about, doesn't it?

HE
(*pretending sympathy*)
Yes, it's very sad.
(*hands her the scissors*)
Well, thank you.

She sees that he is contemplating the gravestone.

SHE
(*indicating the blank side and the space in
front of it*)
Now that's nice . . . there's a place here for you too.

HE
(*with a little laugh*)
Nice?

SHE
(*hurriedly*)
I mean that when the time comes that you can rest
beside her forever. For Eternity.

*He rises. She is aware from his expression that she hasn't struck
the right note and adds quickly:*

SHE

This cemetery's so crowded. Lots of people, they
don't think ahead . . . there won't be room for
them . . . but *your* mind can be at peace. You *know*
there's a place here for you.

*He gives her a look, and tips his hat. It is obvious he is about to
leave.*

SHE
(anxiously, almost blocking his way)
Aren't you going to put some water in the flowers?

HE
(eager to be on his way)
I, I don't think there's any water around . . .

SHE
Oh, sure, over there on the left by the road, there's
a faucet. Didn't you see it?

He shakes his head.

SHE
Oh goodness, I'll show you . . .

He seems reluctant.

SHE
(reproachfully)
You can't leave those poor little flowers without
any water!

He resigns himself, picks up the metal container of flowers and
they start off. During the following they are walking. She realizes
he has noticed her limp.

SHE
An accident. When I was a kid I fell off a roller
coaster at Coney Island. Honest! It was in all the
papers. The leg healed fine though . . . just a
little stiff.

HE
(politely, attempting to make conversation)
Your . . . your father . . . is he nearby?

SHE
Oh no. Pop refused to be in the ground, he's
at home.
(laughs)
I mean his ashes are.
(frowns)
Cremation's a terrible sin, I know—but Pop insisted
on it. To be honest with you, I don't really like it.

She hesitates and looks at him. His expression seems sympathetic.

SHE

It's kind of spooky having your own father . . .
in a jar that you have to dust and all. Right on the
mantelpiece. Know what I mean?

HE

I can imagine.

SHE

I tried putting him in the china closet but my sisters
and brothers had a fit. They said it didn't show the
proper respect.

HE

Well, uh, why didn't they keep the . . . the urn?

SHE

They thought Pop belonged in his own house where
he's always been. Of course it's *my* house now.
  (*with a sideways glance*)
He left it to me. I just rattle around in that big
old place.
  (*another sideways glance*)
It's a very well-built house . . . high ceilings . . .
you know . . . those new apartments . . . they may
be *new* but they have such low ceilings!

HE

I know. I live in one.

SHE

  (*quickly*)
Of course there is something *cozy* about low ceilings.

*They arrive at a faucet at the top of a pipe protruding from the
ground.*

SHE

Here we are!

HE

Well! Looks like I walked right past it.

He turns the faucet and starts to fill the container.

SHE
Guess you're as unfamiliar with this cemetery as
I am.

HE
I don't come as often as I should.

SHE
(*comfortingly*)
A person gets involved with a whole new life—
new friends—
(*then, significantly*)
New family even?

HE
It's a long trip—it's two buses, one subway . . .

*He has filled the container. She opens her handbag and takes
out two paper cups.*

SHE
Care for a drink of water?

HE
(*surprised at the sight of the cups*)
Thanks.

He fills the cups for them both, turns off the faucet. They drink.

SHE
This is the first time I've been in this cemetery . . .
even though I live right near by. I just suddenly
thought to myself—it's a nice peaceful place to take
a walk.

HE
Yes it is peaceful.

His cup is empty. She takes it and puts it inside her own.

SHE
There's a litter basket over there.

*She leads him off around another path. They come to a small
grave, the tombstone decorated with two cherubs. It reads:*

EDWARD DENNIS FOY
BELOVED SON OF
JAMES AND IRENE FOY
1926–1930

SHE
(*shaking her head*)
1926 to 1930!

HE
Foy. Wonder if that's any relation. No, it couldn't be.
Still it could be a nephew or a cousin. Did you ever
hear of a comic named Eddie Foy?

SHE
I don't think so . . .

HE
You're too young.

*She is very pleased. They walk on. She tosses the cups into a
litter basket.*

HE
Eddie Foy was one funny Irishman. All he had to
do was open his mouth and the audience rolled in
the aisles.

SHE
Gee!

HE
I used to play hookey from school to catch his act.
I thought that must be the greatest feeling in the
world . . . to make people laugh. It's like . . . like . . .

SHE
They're all blowing kisses at you!

HE
Yeah, like that! You know one summer when I was
about fifteen I got a job in a theater selling lemonade.
I not only sold it, I made it. We used to make it in
those big tin washbuckets . . . with big chunks of
ice. It wasn't exactly what you'd call sanitary . . . but

nobody got poisoned. That much I know. Anyway, I used to see Eddie Foy's act four times a day.
(*proudly as he thinks back*)
You know once Eddie Foy gave me a nickel for getting his shoes shined. I never spent it. I kept it as a lucky piece.

SHE
Do you still have it?

HE
I lost it a long, long time ago.

SHE
(*with sympathy*)
That's too bad.

His expression changes. His luck hasn't been exactly wonderful since he's grown up.

HE
Wasn't anything magic about it. Just a nickel from Eddie Foy.
(*makes a move to go*)
Well, thanks a lot for showing me the water faucet.

Quickly she opens her purse and scoops out a crumpled bag of peanuts.

SHE
Would you like a peanut?

HE
No thanks.

SHE
It's been so long since lunch, you must be famished!
(*offers the bag again*)

HE
No, really, thank you.

SHE
They're fresh-roasted! Don't you like peanuts?

HE
Yes, I do . . . but you know, they sure put the weight on . . .

SHE
(*with an approving look at him*)
You don't have to worry about that!

HE
They say extra weight puts a strain on the heart.

SHE
But you're not *fat*! Besides I don't think a man looks
very manly—if he's all skin and bones!

*She holds out the bag again. He does like peanuts and he can't
find it in his heart to reject her friendliness.*

HE
Okay, thank you.
(*takes a peanut and pops it in his mouth*)
You know Rose would have a fit if she could see me
eating peanuts.

SHE
(*putting a peanut in her mouth*)
But you have a big frame . . . a man with a big
frame, he needs a few extra pounds.

HE
(*with a glance at the gravestone*)
That's what I used to tell her.

SHE
Just take a little walk after dinner. You'll cancel
those calories right out.

HE
I'm the kind of guy who never walks when he can
stand and never stands when he can sit . . .

*He looks around. There is no place to sit except his wife's grave.
He sits down and gestures to her to sit beside him.*

SHE
(*embarrassed*)
That's all right for you . . . you're a relative. But . . .
would she like a stranger sitting on her resting place?

HE
Be a guest. Rose won't mind.

She crosses over and sits beside him. She offers him the bag of peanuts and during the following they are eating. She is careful to present the bag, offering a new peanut, every time he swallows.

SHE
They're good, aren't they? I practically live on peanuts since Pop died.
(sighs)
Oh, I miss him terribly. It's no fun cooking for yourself . . . even if you can make pastry light as a leaf.

HE
One thing Rose never had in the house was pastry . . . Sometimes I used to sneak out at night for a couple of Danish or some donuts . . .
(glances triumphantly at the gravestone)
Rose never knew . . .

SHE
(laughs)
After all, nobody can smell cake on your breath!

HE
Of course I can eat whatever I want—now that I'm alone.

SHE
(with an almost imperceptible sigh of relief)
You haven't married again?

HE
Rose's old friends are always trying to fix me up. But I've discouraged them.

SHE
Why?

HE
Don't like the candidates. There was this female dentist. First time I went out with her she offered to cap all my front teeth!

SHE
What?

HE

Fifteen hundred dollar job . . . free. How do you
like that for a bribe?

She gives him a shocked look.

HE

Then there was this widow . . . Brownie Krakower.
I told her to stop telephoning me. Know what she
called me?

She shakes her head.

HE

You'll pardon the language, Miss . . .?

SHE

O'Meaghan. Mary O'Meaghan.

HE

She called me a "little fat hairy bastard." . . .
Excuse me.

SHE
(*drawing in her breath, indignant*)
And as I said before, you're not *fat!*

HE
(*really warming towards her now*)
By the way, my name's Belli. Ivor Belli . . . with
an "I."

SHE
(*glancing at the marble headstone*)
Yes, I know.
(*chummily*)
I think it's wonderful to be Italian. My sister
married an Italian. He's full of fun, good-natured
and outgoing. He's crazy about the way I make
spaghetti. Especially with a seafood sauce. You ought
to taste it.

HE

Belli only sounds Italian. I'm Russian.

SHE
(*taken aback—then, quickly*)
Oh, that's wonderful too. I'm sure Russians are just
like everybody else.
(*hurries on*)
Red cabbage soup, hot or cold—with sour cream!
Delicious!
(*reaches into the peanut bag*)
Oh, there's only one left . . .
(*holds it out to him*)
You take it.

He does so.

*A slight pause. Then she glances at the tombstone and reads
aloud.*

SHE
Ivy and Carla. I bet they're cute—aren't they?

He smiles proudly and shrugs.

SHE
Oh be modest! But I'm sure they are. If they favor
their father. You know kids just slay me. I'd trade
any grown-up for any kid. My sister has five, four
girls and a boy. She's always after me to baby-sit.

HE
Well, Ivy's a mother herself and Carla's expecting.

SHE
(*chagrined*)
A grandfather!

HE
That's right.

SHE
You!

HE
I'm fifty-one. Can't say I feel it.

SHE
Fifty-one. That's nothing! That's the prime of life if
you look after yourself. Of course, a man like you,
he needs watching over. It's not good to live alone.

HE
I manage all right.

SHE
A person alone . . . he's apt to forget meals, shirts
without buttons; house gets dusty . . . first thing you
know, they've gone all to seed.

He laughs.

SHE
What are you laughing at?

HE
You sound just like my daughters. Always after me
to move in with them.

SHE
They must be very fond of you.

HE
I like my independence. I don't like to be told what
to do and when to come and go . . .
(*a slightly resentful glance at the gravestone*)
Rose was what you might call a little bossy. She
liked to run things—be in charge.

SHE
I firmly believe a man should be the lord and master
in his own house.

HE
(*quickly*)
Don't get me wrong. She was a wonderful woman . . .

SHE
Oh, I'm sure she was!

HE
She had a wild imagination . . . she got it into her
head that I was interested in my secretary. *More* than
interested, if you follow me.

She nods, all ears.

HE
Esther's been with me since I started in business . . .
twenty-two years. She's a wonderful woman. I never
even took her to lunch until after Rose died.

SHE
(*anxious*)
Your secretary, she . . . she's not married?

HE
No. She never met Mr. Right.

SHE
(*trying hard*)
She must be a great help to you . . . having been
with you so long and all.

HE
She's . . . she's devoted to her job. And to her
hobby. Bowling.

SHE
Do you bowl?

HE
Esther's been encouraging me to take it up, but . . .

SHE
I can't bowl on account of my leg . . . but you'd be
surprised how well I can dance.

HE
I don't dance too well.

SHE
Oh I bet you can.

HE
I mean, not the kind of dancing they do today . . .
all that wiggling and jiggling around.

SHE
I like the real old-fashioned kind—waltzes, and
foxtrots. Dancing is just as good exercise as bowling
and then you have the added advantage of listening
to nice music.

HE
Do you like music?

SHE
(*nods happily*)
You know; I have thousands of old records, well
hundreds. Pop used to work for a record company,
shellacking records . . . until he retired. Do you
remember Helen Morgan?

HE
(*enthusiastic*)
Do I remember Helen Morgan! She was my goddess!
I was crazy about her. That white face and that
black hair! I was *in love* with Helen Morgan!

SHE
(*eagerly*)
She slays me. She just knocks me out! I know all her
songs . . . from listening to her records. Sometimes
like when I'm alone and sort of fed up, I pretend
I'm her. Pretend I'm singing in a nightclub . . .

HE
You remember that she always sat on the piano—

SHE
Could you do me a favor?

HE
If I can, certainly.

She draws in her breath and exhales it slowly.

SHE
(*shyly*)
Would you listen to my imitation and tell me your
honest opinion?

HE
Your imitation of Helen Morgan?

She nods.

SHE
Sure you won't be embarrassed?

HE
No, I'd love to hear it.

SHE
(*shyly*)
All right . . .
(*rises and glances around*)
Since there's nobody around . . .

HE
Go on, sing . . .

She crosses to Rose's gravestone and perches herself up on it.

SHE
You've got to use your imagination. Pretend I'm
sitting on a piano—
  (*suddenly aware she is sitting on Rose's stone
  she utters a little exclamation and leaps off*)
Oh, I'm sorry, Mr. Belli.

HE
It's okay . . . Forget it . . . It's all right . . .

He motions her to get back up on the stone. Reassured, she does.

SHE
Well I'm sitting on a piano . . . and the spotlight is
shining down on me . . .

*She tilts her chin upwards, her head back and assumes what she
believes to be a romantic posture. She sucks in her cheeks and
parts her lips. She waits, as if listening to the music to cue her.
She sings in a small sweet, vulnerable voice, rather like Helen
Morgan's in tone and phrasing.*

FOR MY SAKE

My arms, you've been empty long enough,
What good are arms when there's no man to hold?
If one should pass by, I beg you unfold,
For my sake, arms,
Reach and unfold!

My eyes, you've been guarded long enough,
What good are eyes with no glance meeting mine?
If he should stop here, I beg you to shine,
For my sake, eyes,
Soften and shine!

Let me feel again
Be alive and real again
Head over heel again . . .
Let me try again,
Radiant and high again,
Or learn to cry again . . .

My heart, you've been peaceful long enough,
What good's a heart with no reason to ache?
If he should roam on, I want you to break,
For my sake, heart,
Shatter and break . . . shatter and break.

*As she comes to the end of the song, unnoticed by both of them
a mother and two children pass by. One of the children giggles.*

CHILD
What is that lady doing?

MOTHER
(glaring at Mary on the gravestone)
Disgraceful! Some people have no respect!

Mother turns her back and marches her children off.

HE
I'm sorry. Silly kid.

*She has slipped off the stone and now stands in front of him close
to tears.*

SHE
I feel so ashamed.

HE
What for? That was beautiful! I mean it!
(she shakes her head)
I really do. You can sing.

SHE
(her voice breaking)
That's very sweet of you to say so . . .

HE
Believe me I was touched. It brought back my whole
youth.

She wipes her eyes. Suddenly her face brightens.

SHE
(softly)
Mr. Belli . . . I've got a good idea . . . Why don't you
come over to my house for dinner? Any date you
pick . . .
(she doesn't notice his wary glance)

I'll plan all the food really Russian and I'll sing to
you all you want! And we can play records. Helen
Morgan records.

HE

Thank you, Miss O'Meaghan. That's something to
look forward to.
    (*arches his back a bit*)
You know, sitting on cold stone too long . . . you can
catch something.

He stands and adjusts his coat.

SHE

When could you come to dinner?

HE

I don't think I could make it very soon. I'm way
behind in my work. You know what happens to us
tax fellows in April . . .

SHE

Oh you just pick any time that you'll be free and I'll
see to it that I'm free too . . .

HE

I'll be working nights for a long time. I don't think
I'd better commit myself right now . . .
    (*she realizes that he is rejecting her invitation*)
I'd better be getting back to the office. It's late.
Esther'll give me hell.

SHE

    (*trying to hide her hurt*)
Your secretary?

HE

She'll probably have phone messages waiting for me
and all that. She has a fit when I'm not there to
close the office with her.

SHE

You're the *boss*, aren't you?

HE

Esther keeps a tight rein on me.
    (*he laughs*)
She's a lot like Rose in that respect. Esther made me
wear this top coat. Esther says it's not Spring until
she says it's Spring.

SHE
(*intense with anxiety*)
Mr. Belli, I don't want you to think I ask just *anyone*
to dinner . . .

HE
Of course not! You're really a very *likeable* person . . .

SHE
Maybe you won't think so because of what I'm going
to do . . .
(*he raises his eyebrows*)
I want to ask you a very personal question.
(*quickly with all the courage she has*)
Mr. Belli, have you considered marrying again?

HE
(*clearing his throat to gain time*)
At my age? By the way, I told you a little fib before.
I'm not fifty-one—I'm fifty-five—and who the hell
would want me?

SHE
I'm sure many women would want you, Mr. Belli.

HE
I *was* married . . . twenty-seven years. That's enough
for any lifetime.

The color has drained from her face. He fumbles on.

HE
Listen, I—all I want is my TV, some beer. Poker
one a week. I . . . I . . . don't want to be responsible
for a puppy even . . . or a cat . . .

She is staring at him, her face pale. He coughs and raises his hat.

HE
It's certainly been very pleasant meeting you,
Miss O'Meaghan.

SHE
(*attempting a smile*)
Same here.
(*desperately, as he starts off*)
Mind if I walk with you to the gate?

HE
A pleasure.

They stroll along a path among the graves. He adjusts his pace to her limp. During the following they are walking through the cemetery.

> SHE
>
> Since my father died my whole family's been at me to get married. "Poor Mary, what's to become of her? A grown woman doesn't know how to type, take shorthand—can't even wait on table because of her leg—" All I heard was "Mary, why don't you get married."

> HE
>
> Why fight that? You're a fine person—you should be married. You'd make some man a wonderful wife.

> SHE
>
> Sure I would. But *who*?

She flings her arm towards Manhattan, the country, the continent.

> SHE
>
> Especially if . . . if you're just an ordinary person like me.

> HE
>
> No, no, not at all. You're not ordinary. Couldn't you do something with your talent? Your voice?

> SHE
>
> (*clasping and unclasping her handbag*)
> Don't poke fun, please. I *am* ordinary.
> (*a pause*)
> But so is my friend Annie Austin.
> (*sighs*)
> Funny, isn't it? The things that work out for one person don't necessarily work out for another person.

> HE
>
> How . . . do you mean?

> SHE
>
> She met both her husbands in a cemetery.

> HE
>
> (*startled*)
> Both?

SHE

Mr. Cruikshank. And after he ran away, Mr. Austin.
So you see, for her it worked out.

HE

But . . . how did she happen to be in a cemetery?

SHE

She went there on purpose.
(*he gives her a puzzled look*)
First she'd read the obituary columns and then she'd
go to some funerals—sort of hung around and
introduced herself and sympathized. That didn't
work out so well because the families are there, you
know . . . watching like hawks. So then she hit on
this idea of just going to cemeteries. On a nice day
she'd come here or go to Woodlawn. There are
always widowers walking around thinking how much
they miss home life and wishing they were married
again . . .

*He stops and throws his head back bursting into loud laughter.
She joins him, laughing too.*

SHE

(*after a moment, hardly able to catch her breath*)
Even I can see the humor of it!
(*more laughter from them both*)
But it does sound *sensible,* don't you think?

HE

(*highly amused*)
Yes I do.

SHE

That's why I'm here today. I wanted to try it myself.

They walk along.

SHE

I wish you would tell me frankly—how does a
woman find a husband, if she's not young and pretty?

HE

(*a pause, then suddenly*)
Esther's not young and pretty . . .

He seems surprised at what he has just said. For the first time it is clear to him that he has, without knowing it, been planning to marry Esther for a long time.

> SHE
> *(with an understanding glance at him)*
> I guess you two have a lot in common?

> HE
> *(thoughtfully)*
> Yes, yes, we do.

> SHE
> It sounds like a terrific combination . . . the two
> of you.
> *(he nods. She sighs slightly)*
> Guess I'll just have to keep trying. I'm not lazy by
> nature.

> HE
> You'll find someone. A livelier fellow than me . . .

They are approaching the gates of the cemetery and he sees she is looking at a man who is just entering. He is a little man spouting cheery whistlings and with a snap to his step. There is a black band sewn around the sleeve of his coat. He is carrying a bunch of red tulips.

> SHE
> *(staring)*
> My, those flowers are pretty! I'm very partial to
> tulips myself!

They are at the gate. He raises his hat. She has turned her head to watch the direction taken by the newcomer.

> HE
> Good luck, Miss O'Meaghan . . .

They smile at each other. She starts courageously off after the little man.

> HE
> *(calling)*
> And thanks for the peanuts!

LONG SLOW DISSOLVE TO A Christmas Memory

MARY O'MEAGHAN *Maureen Stapleton*   IVOR BELLI *Martin Balsam*

film credits

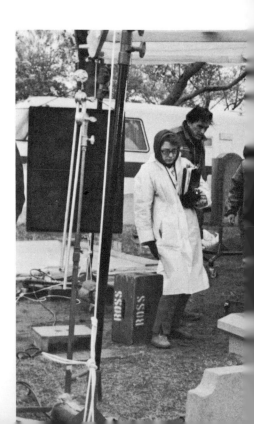

DIRECTOR/PRODUCER *Frank Perry*
SCREENPLAY *Truman Capote & Eleanor Perry*
MUSIC *Meyer Kupferman*
PHOTOGRAPHY *Joseph Brun, A.S.C.*
PRODUCTION DESIGNER *Peter Dohanos*
FILM EDITOR *Patricia Jaffe*
IN CHARGE OF PRODUCTION *Joel Glickman*
ASSISTANT TO MR. PERRY *Lynn Forman*
COSTUME DESIGNER *Frank Thompson*
RECORDING SUPERVISOR *Dick Vorisek*
ASSISTANT DIRECTORS *Stanley Ackerman & George Goodman*
WARDROBE *Marilyn Putnam*
SCRIPT SUPERVISOR *Kay Chapin*
SET DECORATOR *Leif Pedersen*
SOUND *Chuck Federmack & Nat Boxer*
CAMERA OPERATOR *Peter Garbarini*
Song FOR MY SAKE *Lyric by Eleanor Perry/
Music by Meyer Kupferman*

Among the Paths to Eden was originally televised by the American
Broadcasting Company on December 17, 1967. It received numer-
ous prizes and citations including an Emmy Award for Maureen
Stapleton's portrayal of the woman.

Among the

Paths to Eden

notes

Our major problem in this adaptation was how to extend the story to fill fifty-two minutes of television screen time. We all agreed that the ideal length for this play would be about a half hour. Actually the theatrical film version is twenty-five minutes long and has benefited from the cutting.

The characters themselves were not the problem. Fifty-two minutes is a short time in which to examine two human beings in depth. The major drawback was the limiting setting. Limiting, that is, for our two characters. We can imagine a long series of activities that could take place in a cemetery—anything from dueling to love making to plotting a revolution—but Mary O'Meaghan and Ivor Belli being who they are were unlikely to engage in any activities beyond sitting, standing or walking. Since not much "behavior" was possible for them we would have to depend entirely on talk to hold the audience's interest for almost an hour. Naturally we worried about coming up with a very talky show.

thoughts into dialogue

A valuable part of the adaptor's work is to use material which the prose writer has narrated either from his own omniscient point of view or as part of the character's thoughts. The following are some examples in this script:

The sequence on page 135 as the man thinks about the women who have pursued him becomes the dialogue in the film on pages 155 and 156.

The man's thoughts on page 128 about what Sarah would say if she could see him shelling peanuts on her grave, gave us the idea for the exchange about gaining weight on page 154.

In the script as in the story the man's vague feelings about his secretary are finally focused onto the idea of marrying her by Mary's question "Have you considered marrying again?" In the story this decision is narrated. We wanted to get the point across in the script without having him come right out and say it. We have him mention Esther a couple of times to indicate that she is very much on his mind (also we have an opportunity to show what kind of person she is—bossy like his dead wife: "Esther says it isn't Spring until *she says* it's Spring"). And finally the moment of his decision is dramatized when Mary asks, ". . . how does a woman find a husband when she's not young and pretty?" and he answers "Esther's not young and pretty" (page 167). This is a wonderfully acted moment as we see the realization on the actor's face that he will indeed marry Esther. Everything has finally clicked into place including his compulsion to repeat himself—to marry another dominating woman. We didn't have him state it aloud because he is much too tactful to do so, he feels too much compassion about Mary.

characterization

Unlike Miriam this story gives us a lot of information about our two major characters.

For example, Ivor appears to have settled for a bossy wife, two conventional daughters and a fairly commonplace career as an accountant. But, like everyone else, in his youth at least, he must have had dreams and fantasies. In the first draft of the TV filmplay, Ivor tells Mary he had once wanted to be a stand-up comic like Eddie Foy. He relates an anecdote in which he finally got a job at a resort hotel but the first time he got up to do his act he had such stage fright he forgot all the punch lines. It's both a funny and a sad story. This passage was eventually cut but a remnant of it remains in the script where he talks about Eddie Foy: "I thought that must be one of the greatest feelings in the world . . . to make people laugh" (page 151) and a little later when Mary sympathizes with him because he lost the nickel Foy gave him, he cuts her off sharply, "Wasn't anything magic about it . . ." (page 152). On the screen we see a fleetingly desolate expression on the actor's face and although in this version we don't know precisely why, it doesn't matter. What we do know is that he is thinking about the past, with some hurt.

the song

Naturally we wanted Mary to sing one of the songs associated with the career of Helen Morgan: "Mean to Me," "Don't Ever Leave Me," "My Bill." Because the royalty payments were exorbitant, this turned out to be impossible. The only alternative was to write one. "For My Sake" is my attempt at an imitation Helen Morgan ballad in which I tried to fit the lyric to Mary's situation.

extending the story

For the TV-film version we decided to add about twenty minutes of new material at the beginning of the show. We expanded the cast of characters, and allowed Mary O'Meaghan to become involved with them as she wanders through the cemetery and before she meets Ivor Belli.

First she stops to talk to two grave diggers who are rather cheerily going about their job. (One is a bachelor but it becomes clear in the dialogue that he intends to remain that way.) Next, Mary tags along behind a funeral procession where she finds out it is a *man* who is being buried. She hurries off. Finally she joins a group of mourners at an open grave.

Because of Mary's unsophistication there are several comedic cross-currents in the dialogue and a gag-line blackout at the end. This sequence, as played, was extremely funny but it is a self contained skit, not really appropriate to the gentle drama of the original story. We realized this but we kept it anyway for humor and for length.

These opening scenes which appear in the television version only follow.

Mary O'Meaghan, walking slowly down a long, straight path, surrounded by tombstones, Manhattan far in the distance, comes upon two gravediggers, their lunchboxes open beside them, eating lunch on the grass. A few feet away is a half dug grave. One of the gravediggers is about fifty. The other is a good looking, strong young man in his early twenties. She stops and gives them a friendly smile.

SHE
My, it's a nice day for a picnic, isn't it?

OLDER DIGGER
(*pleasantly*)
Always glad when Spring comes in our line of
work. Ground softens up . . .

SHE
(*glancing at the open grave*)
Must be . . . very strenuous. All that . . . uh . . .
digging.

OLDER DIGGER
It's okay. Healthy exercise in the open air, no
seasonal lay-offs.

SHE
Seasonal lay-offs?

OLDER DIGGER
Ain't no time of the year people stops dyin'.

YOUNG DIGGER
Some winters with pneumonia and we all make
good overtime.

SHE
Well, now . . . that's nice for you, isn't it?
(*another glance at the grave*)
Uh . . . when do you expect the funeral?

OLDER DIGGER
Tomorrow, I think. You could get all that
information over at the cemetery office . . .
(*he gestures*)

SHE
Oh, I was just wondering . . .

OLDER DIGGER
Loretta, she's the receptionist up there . . . she'd
be glad to tell you . . .

SHE
I wouldn't want to appear nosy.
(*with a bright smile*)

Actually I'm just out for a little walk. I only live
a few blocks away and it suddenly occurred to me,
why not take a walk in the cemetery! Maybe that
sounds funny to you? Taking a walk in a cemetery?

> OLDER DIGGER
> (*politely*)

Not at all . . .

> SHE

It's not so different from a park, is it? Grass and
flowers. And of course it's quieter.

> OLDER DIGGER

A *lot* quieter.

> SHE

I lost my Pop recently . . .

> OLDER DIGGER

I'm sorry to hear that.

> SHE

I spent all my time taking care of him so now
I'm . . . well, I'm sort of on my own.

Older Digger, his mouth full of sandwich, nods.

> SHE

All my brothers and sisters got married . . . I was
the only one left who could take care of Pop.

> OLDER DIGGER

That's something you'll never regret, Ma'm.

*Young Digger has been rummaging through his lunchbox. He
has a hard-boiled egg in one hand.*

> YOUNG DIGGER

No salt! Can ya beat that? This is the first time
she forgot to pack the salt!

> OLDER DIGGER
> (*grinning*)

Honeymoon is over, son.

*She opens her handbag, takes out a miniature, cardboard, blue
Morton's salt shaker and hands it to the Young Digger.*

> YOUNG DIGGER
> (*surprised*)

Why thank you Ma'm. Sure appreciate it.

> SHE
> (*gaily*)

I carry it for popcorn. In the movies.

*The Young Digger hands the salt back to her. She offers it to
the Older Digger.*

> SHE

Want some?

> OLDER DIGGER

No thanks.

> SHE
> (*craning her neck to peer into his lunchbox*)

I guess your . . . wife is more experienced?

> OLDER DIGGER

I'm a bachelor.

> SHE

Oh? Who packs your lunch?

OLDER DIGGER

I do. Same thing every day of the year.
(*shows her*)
One ham, one cheese, one cruller, one cupcake.

SHE

That's not very well balanced.

OLDER DIGGER
(*shrugs*)
Don't see no one diggin' *my* grave.

SHE

You should have something hot . . . like a thermos
of vegetable soup or pork and beans . . . maybe
even a good ox-tail stew . . .

OLDER DIGGER
(*with a laugh*)
That's what Loretta says . . . Loretta up at the
cemetery office.

SHE

Well, she's right.

OLDER DIGGER

Nah, she's got her cap set for me. I'm on to her
tricks.

SHE

Looking after a man's health isn't a trick!

OLDER DIGGER

It is if you wanna catch him and he doesn't wanna
get caught.

SHE
(*wilting*)
Well, I . . . uh, I'd better be going along . . .

(*another look at the grave*)
Uh, could you tell me . . . uh, is that for a man
or a woman?

OLDER DIGGER

We dig 'em . . . we don't book 'em, Ma'm.

YOUNG DIGGER

Go over to the office and ask Loretta, why don't you?

SHE
(quickly)
No, no, I was just . . . curious.
(she laughs)
Curiosity killed the cat!
(with a bright little wave)
Well, nice to have met you both.

OLDER DIGGER
Likewise, Ma'm.

As she walks off, the Two Diggers raise their eyebrows at each other.

She turns down another path and sees several yards ahead a funeral cortege slowly winding its way between the gravestones. She hurries her steps to catch up with it. There are about two dozen mourners following the coffin. A severe looking gray-haired couple past middle age are bringing up the rear. They turn to look at her briefly as she falls into step behind them.

MAN
(to his wife)
Well here's one more, thank heavens.

WOMAN
(turning to Mary)
Did you happen to see if anyone else was coming along?

She glances back briefly and shakes her head.

WOMAN
(to her husband)
Disgraceful! People have no respect.

During the following exchanges, the husband and wife turn to address all their remarks to Mary. She reacts with appropriate expressions, now and then clicking her tongue, etc.

WOMAN
I was just saying people have no respect these days.

MAN
There were hundreds at the funeral service and look!
(he gestures at the small line of mourners)

WOMAN

People can take time to drink martinis and watch
television and chase after autographs from
Hollywood stars . . . but they can't take time to
accompany the remains!

MAN

We went to a funeral last week and there were
only nine people at the final resting place.

WOMAN

Except for the pall bearers and the minister,
of course.

MAN

If a thing's worth doing, it's worth doing right.

WOMAN

All I can say is my heart goes out to that poor widow.

SHE
(speaking for the first time)
Widow?
(she stops in her tracks)

The cortege is turning a corner. At the front of the line we can
see a woman dressed in black, her head shrouded in a black veil.

WOMAN
(peers at the widow . . . then, to her husband)
Such a dear fragile little thing. I don't know what
she's going to do without him.

MAN

Be married in a year.

WOMAN
(an angry whisper)
Please don't be coarse at a time like this . . .

The Man and Woman glance behind them to see if this alterca-
tion has been overheard by Mary. They are astounded. She is
nowhere in sight.

She is standing in the place where the cortege turned off, gazing
alertly in the opposite direction. We see quite a large number of
mourners clustered in a tight group around a grave. The mourn-

ers are several rows thick. Apart from the rest and standing separately are a half dozen men and women, their heads bowed.

She walks towards the group of mourners cautiously and circles around them obviously trying to case the scene.

From the head of the grave comes a ministerial voice pronouncing the words of the service. She moves in a little closer standing on tiptoe to see what she can see. She moves in closer yet. She finds herself beside one of the mourners who is standing separately from the others. He is staring into the distance. She looks him over shyly. He is a tall, impeccably dressed man of about forty. He wears a dark suit and an expensive looking coat flung over his shoulders. She stares sideways at him shyly but approvingly and waits for him to notice her. When he does she gives him a tiny sympathetic smile.

> SHE
> It's a very sad occasion, isn't it?

> FIRST MAN
> Wouldn't feel as bad if my own mother died.

> SHE
> (*a beat*)
> Was she your . . . your stepmother?

> FIRST MAN
> I think of her as my *good* mother.

> SHE
> Oh dear, it's a shame, isn't it?
> (*a beat, then casually*)
> I suppose the . . . the widower is up there . . .
> beside the grave?

> FIRST MAN
> (*viciously*)
> I wish he were in it!

She looks at him, bewildered.

> FIRST MAN
> Excuse me, if you're a relative.

> SHE
> No, no, not a relative.

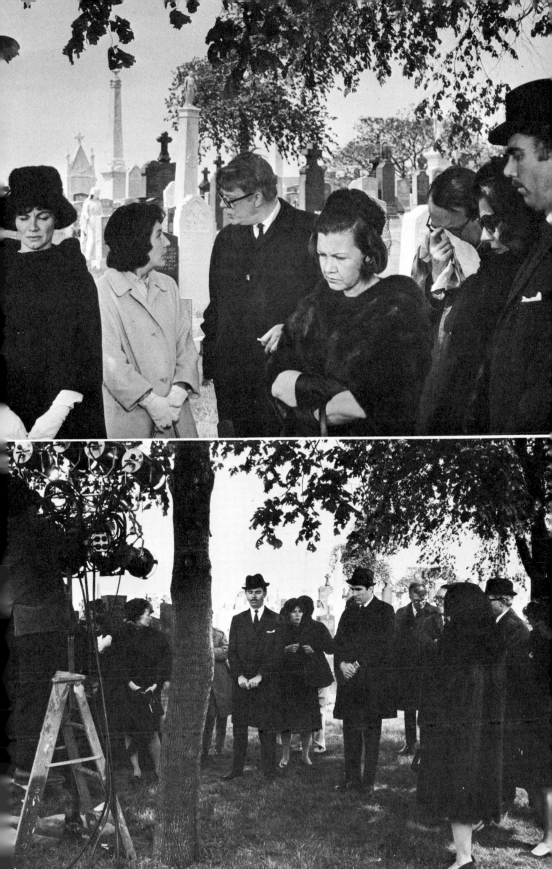

FIRST MAN
(*showing a little more interest in her*)
It's really worse for the ones like us, isn't it?

SHE
Us?

FIRST MAN
Our bonds to her are stronger than blood.

First Man indicates a small man nearby. His thin shoulders are shaking, his weeping face pressed into a handkerchief.

FIRST MAN
Look at him. He's one of us.

SHE
(*gazing at Weeping Man*)
He's very . . . affected, isn't he?

FIRST MAN
(*giving the weeping man a furious look*)
If there's anything I can't *stand* . . . it's an emotional outburst in public.
(*he turns back to her*)
How long were you in?

She looks puzzled.

FIRST MAN
How long did you know her?

SHE
I didn't really know her. I'm just . . . uh . . . just an observer.

FIRST MAN
That's how I feel. Detached.

SHE
I . . . uh . . . was sort of . . . taking a walk through the cemetery.

FIRST MAN
Exactly the kind of thing I've been telling myself. Defense mechanism, of course.

SHE
Beg pardon?

FIRST MAN

If we didn't have these fantasies we'd be screaming
and tearing our hair.
(another harsh look at the weeping man)
I keep all my feelings locked inside. That's my
problem.

SHE
(a beat as she thinks this over . . .
unsuccessfully)
Are you uh . . . here alone?

FIRST MAN
(coldly)
We're all alone on this planet, aren't we?

SHE
(another beat)
What I mean is . . . is anyone here with you?
(she adds timidly)
Your . . . wife or anyone?

FIRST MAN

My wife's probably drinking champagne in some
bar . . . celebrating this funeral.

SHE
(aghast)
Oh no. Why?

FIRST MAN

My wife never wanted me to become a mature
aggressive dominant male. Would any woman?
Would *you*?

He gives her an icy hateful glare and resumes staring into the
distance. She looks up at him in total confusion. Finally she
shrugs and sidles away. She almost bumps into another man
also standing by himself nearby. This one is in his late thirties,
dressed in a baggy corduroy suit and a black turtle neck sweater.
His eyes have been squeezed shut with anguish. When she
bumps into him he opens them and stares at her.

SHE
Oh, I . . . I beg your pardon . . .

Second man shuts his eyes again and again his face screws up into a mask of agony.

> SHE
> (*worried*)
> Did I . . . step on your toe?

He doesn't seem to have heard.

> SHE
> I just want to say . . . I'm terribly sorry about your grief.

> SECOND MAN
> (*without opening his eyes*)
> There's no justice in the world, baby.

She turns to see if he is addressing someone else.

> SHE
> (*shyly*)
> I lost my Pop recently. I know how you feel . . .

> SECOND MAN
> Don't give me that understanding crap. I'm not on *your* couch.

> SHE
> Are you . . . uh . . . a son of the deceased?

> SECOND MAN
> Her son, her brother, her lover, her father . . . I've been them all.

She blinks, unable to follow him.

> SECOND MAN
> (*he squeezes his eyes shut again*)
> Oh the pain of it! The *exquisite* pain of it!

> SHE
> How did it . . . happen? If you don't mind my asking?

> SECOND MAN
> That creep she's married to skidded . . . rammed the car into a tree. Ghastly irony! *He's* got a broken leg!

SHE
Poor thing.

SECOND MAN
Poor thing? He *killed* her, for God's sake!

SHE
(*horrified*)
I thought it was an accident.

SECOND MAN
(*with a looney smile*)
As Freud said, there *are* no accidents!

During the above the ministerial voice has stopped and the cluster of mourners is beginning to break up.

SHE
(*hastily*)
Well now . . . that we've gotten acquainted a bit I
hope we'll meet again sometime. When you visit
her grave?

SECOND MAN
Visit her grave? I'll *dance* on her grave!

SHE
But I thought . . .

SECOND MAN
I'm extremely hostile towards women . . . that's my
problem.

He turns on his heel and stalks off. She looks after him mystified. All the mourners are quite a distance up the path now except the Weeping Man. He is walking very slowly, his face still buried in his handkerchief. She hurries to catch up with him.

SHE
Would you like a cup of tea to cheer you up?

He shakes his head without lifting it from the handkerchief.

SHE
I kept some brandy in the house when my Pop was
sick. Would you like some brandy?
(*same business from the Man*)
I wish I could do something to help you.
(*same business from the Man*)

SHE
I just want you to know I do sympathize with you
in your loss.

WEEPING MAN
(*raises his head from his handkerchief and
glares at her*)
What do you know about my loss?

SHE
(*startled*)
Of your . . . your loved one.

WEEPING MAN
She wasn't my loved one. She was my head doctor.

SHE
Your what?

WEEPING MAN
My psychoanalyst. Twelve thousand dollars I
invested in that woman. Twelve thousand dollars!
That's my loss.

Man puts his face back into his handkerchief and walks on.

A Christmas Memory

the story

IMAGINE A MORNING in late November. A coming of winter morning more than twenty years ago. Consider the kitchen of a spreading old house in a country town. A great black stove is its main feature; but there is also a big round table and a fireplace with two rocking chairs placed in front of it. Just today the fireplace commenced its seasonal roar.

A woman with shorn white hair is standing at the kitchen window. She is wearing tennis shoes and a shapeless gray sweater over a summery calico dress. She is small and sprightly, like a bantam hen; but, due to a long youthful illness, her shoulders are pitifully hunched. Her face is remarkable—not unlike Lincoln's, craggy like that, and tinted by sun and wind; but it is delicate too, finely boned, and her eyes are sherry-colored and timid. "Oh my," she exclaims, her breath smoking the windowpane, "it's fruitcake weather!"

The person to whom she is speaking is myself. I am seven; she is sixty-something. We are cousins, very distant ones, and we have lived together—well, as long as I can remember. Other people inhabit the house, relatives; and though they have power over us, and frequently make us cry, we are not, on the whole, too much aware of them. We are each other's best friend. She calls me Buddy, in memory of a boy who was formerly her best friend. The other Buddy died in the 1880's, when she was still a child. She is still a child.

"I knew it before I got out of bed," she says, turning away

from the window with a purposeful excitement in her eyes. "The courthouse bell sounded so cold and clear. And there were no birds singing; they've gone to warmer country, yes indeed. Oh, Buddy, stop stuffing biscuits and fetch our buggy. Help me find my hat. We've thirty cakes to bake."

It's always the same: a morning arrives in November, and my friend, as though officially inaugurating the Christmas time of year that exhilarates her imagination and fuels the blaze of her heart, announces: "It's fruitcake weather! Fetch our buggy. Help me find my hat."

The hat is found, a straw cartwheel corsaged with velvet roses out-of-doors has faded: it once belonged to a more fashionable relative. Together, we guide our buggy, a dilapidated baby carriage, out to the garden and into a grove of pecan trees. The buggy is mine; that is, it was bought for me when I was born. It is made of wicker, rather unraveled, and the wheels wobble like a drunkard's legs. But it is a faithful object; springtimes, we take it to the woods and fill it with flowers, herbs, wild fern for our porch pots; in the summer, we pile it with picnic paraphernalia and sugar-cane fishing poles and roll it down to the edge of a creek; it has its winter uses, too: as a truck for hauling firewood from the yard to the kitchen, as a warm bed for Queenie, our tough little orange and white rat terrier who has survived distemper and two rattlesnake bites. Queenie is trotting beside it now.

Three hours later we are back in the kitchen hulling a heaping buggyload of windfall pecans. Our backs hurt from gathering them: how hard they were to find (the main crop having been shaken off the trees and sold by the orchard's owners, who are not us) among the concealing leaves, the frosted, deceiving grass. Caarackle! A cheery crunch, scraps of miniature thunder sound as the shells collapse and the golden mound of sweet oily ivory meat mounts in the milk-glass bowl. Queenie begs to taste, and now and again my friend sneaks her a mite, though insisting we deprive ourselves. "We mustn't, Buddy. If we start, we won't stop. And there's scarcely enough as there is. For thirty cakes." The kitchen is growing dark. Dusk turns the window into a mirror: our reflections mingle with the rising moon as we work by the fireside in the firelight. At last, when the moon is quite high, we toss the final hull into the fire and, with joined sighs, watch it catch flame. The buggy is empty, the bowl is brimful.

We eat our supper (cold biscuits, bacon, blackberry jam) and discuss tomorrow. Tomorrow the kind of work I like best begins: buying. Cherries and citron, ginger and vanilla and canned Hawaiian pineapple, rinds and raisins and walnuts and whiskey and oh, so much flour, butter, so many eggs, spices, flavorings: why, we'll need a pony to pull the buggy home.

But before these purchases can be made, there is the question of money. Neither of us has any. Except for skinflint sums persons in the house occasionally provide (a dime is considered very big money); or what we earn ourselves from various activities: holding rummage sales, selling buckets of hand-picked blackberries, jars of homemade jam and apple jelly and peach preserves, rounding up flowers for funerals and weddings. Once we won seventy-ninth prize, five dollars, in a national football contest. Not that we know a fool thing about football. It's just that we enter any contest we hear about: at the moment our hopes are centered on the fifty-thousand-dollar Grand Prize being offered to name a new brand of coffee (we suggested "A.M."; and, after some hesitation, for my friend thought it perhaps sacrilegious, the slogan "A.M.! Amen!"). To tell the truth, our only *really* profitable enterprise was the Fun and Freak Museum we conducted in a back-yard woodshed two summers ago. The Fun was a stereopticon with slide views of Washington and New York lent us by a relative who had been to those places (she was furious when she discovered why we'd borrowed it); the Freak was a three-legged biddy chicken hatched by one of our own hens. Everybody hereabouts wanted to see that biddy: we charged grownups a nickel, kids two cents. And took in a good twenty dollars before the museum shut down due to the decease of the main attraction.

But one way and another we do each year accumulate Christmas savings, a Fruitcake Fund. These moneys we keep hidden in an ancient bead purse under a loose board under the floor under a chamber pot under my friend's bed. The purse is seldom removed from this safe location except to make a deposit, or, as happens every Saturday, a withdrawal; for on Saturdays I am allowed ten cents to go to the picture show. My friend has never been to a picture show, nor does she intend to: "I'd rather hear you tell the story, Buddy. That way I can imagine it more. Besides, a person my age shouldn't squander their eyes. When the Lord comes, let me see him clear." In addition to never having seen a movie, she has never: eaten in a restaurant, traveled more than five miles from home, received or sent a telegram, read anything except funny papers and the Bible, worn cosmetics, cursed, wished someone harm, told a lie on purpose, let a hungry dog go hungry. Here are a few things she has done, does do: killed with a hoe the biggest rattlesnake ever seen in this county (sixteen rattles), dip snuff (secretly), tame hummingbirds (just try it) till they balance on her finger, tell ghost stories (we both believe in ghosts) so tingling they chill you in July, talk to herself, take walks in the rain, grow the prettiest japonicas in town, know the recipe for every sort of old-time Indian cure, including a magical wart-remover.

Now, with supper finished, we retire to the room in a faraway part of the house where my friend sleeps in a scrap-quilt-covered iron bed painted rose pink, her favorite color. Silently, wallowing in the pleasures of conspiracy, we take the bead purse from its secret place and spill its contents on the scrap quilt. Dollar bills, tightly rolled and green as May buds. Somber fifty-cent pieces, heavy enough to weight a dead man's eyes. Lovely dimes, the liveliest coin, the one that really jingles. Nickels and quarters, worn smooth as creek pebbles. But mostly a hateful heap of bitter-odored pennies. Last summer others in the house contracted to pay us a penny for every twenty-five flies we killed. Oh, the carnage of August: the flies that flew to heaven! Yet it was not work in which we took pride. And, as we sit counting pennies, it is as though we were back tabulating dead flies. Neither of us has a head for figures; we count slowly, lose track, start again. According to her calculations, we have $12.73. According to mine, exactly $13. "I do hope you're wrong, Buddy. We can't mess around with thirteen. The cakes will fall. Or put somebody in the cemetery. Why, I wouldn't dream of getting out of bed on the thirteenth." This is true: she always spends thirteenths in bed. So, to be on the safe side, we subtract a penny and toss it out the window.

Of the ingredients that go into our fruitcakes, whiskey is

the most expensive, as well as the hardest to obtain: State laws forbid its sale. But everybody knows you can buy a bottle from Mr. Haha Jones. And the next day, having completed our more prosaic shopping, we set out for Mr. Haha's business address, a "sinful" (to quote public opinion) fish-fry and dancing café down by the river. We've been there before, and on the same errand; but in previous years our dealings have been with Haha's wife, an iodine-dark Indian woman with brazzy peroxided hair and a dead-tired disposition. Actually, we've never laid eyes on her husband, though we've heard that he's an Indian too. A giant with razor scars across his cheeks. They call him Haha because he's so gloomy, a man who never laughs. As we approach his café (a large log cabin festooned inside and out with chains of garish-gay naked lightbulbs and standing by the river's muddy edge under the shade of river trees where moss drifts through the branches like gray mist) our steps slow down. Even Queenie stops prancing and sticks close by. People have been murdered in Haha's café. Cut to pieces. Hit on the head. There's a case coming up in court next month. Naturally these goings-on happen at night when the colored lights cast crazy patterns and the victrola wails. In the daytime Haha's is shabby and deserted. I knock at the door, Queenie barks, my friend calls: "Mrs. Haha, ma'am? Anyone to home?"

Footsteps. The door opens. Our hearts overturn. It's Mr. Haha Jones himself! And he *is* a giant; he *does* have scars; he *doesn't* smile. No, he glowers at us through Satan-tilted eyes and demands to know: "What you want with Haha?"

For a moment we are too paralyzed to tell. Presently my friend half-finds her voice, a whispery voice at best: "If you please, Mr. Haha, we'd like a quart of your finest whiskey."

His eyes tilt more. Would you believe it? Haha is smiling! Laughing, too. "Which one of you is a drinkin' man?"

"It's for making fruitcakes, Mr. Haha. Cooking."

This sobers him. He frowns. "That's no way to waste good whiskey." Nevertheless, he retreats into the shadowed café and seconds later appears carrying a bottle of daisy yellow unlabeled liquor. He demonstrates its sparkle in the sunlight and says: "Two dollars."

We pay him with nickels and dimes and pennies. Suddenly, jangling the coins in his hand like a fistful of dice, his face softens. "Tell you what," he proposes, pouring the money back into our bead purse, "just send me one of them fruitcakes instead."

"Well," my friend remarks on our way home, "there's a lovely man. We'll put an extra cup of raisins in *his* cake."

The black stove, stoked with coal and firewood, glows like a lighted pumpkin. Eggbeaters whirl, spoons spin round in bowls of butter and sugar, vanilla sweetens the air, ginger spices it; melting, nose-tingling odors saturate the kitchen, suffuse the house, drift out to the world on puffs of chimney smoke. In four days our work is done. Thirty-one cakes, dampened with whiskey, bask on window sills and shelves.

Who are they for?

Friends. Not necessarily neighbor friends: indeed, the larger share are intended for persons we've met maybe once, perhaps not at all. People who've struck our fancy. Like President Roosevelt. Like the Reverend and Mrs. J. C. Lucey, Baptist missionaries to Borneo who lectured here last winter. Or the little knife grinder who comes through town twice a year. Or Abner Packer, the driver of the six o'clock bus from Mobile, who exchanges waves with us every day as he passes in a dust-cloud whoosh. Or the young Wistons, a California couple whose car one afternoon broke down outside the house and who spent a pleasant hour chatting with us on the porch (young Mr. Wiston snapped our picture, the only one we've ever had taken). Is it because my friend is shy with everyone *except* strangers that these strangers, and merest acquaintances, seem to us our truest friends? I think yes. Also, the scrapbooks we keep of thank-you's on White House stationery, time-to-time communications from California and Borneo, the knife grinder's penny post cards, make us feel connected to eventful worlds beyond the kitchen with its view of a sky that stops.

Now a nude December fig branch grates against the window. The kitchen is empty, the cakes are gone; yesterday we carted the last of them to the post office, where the cost of stamps turned our purse inside out. We're broke. That rather depresses me, but my friend insists on celebrating—with two inches of whiskey left in Haha's bottle. Queenie has a spoonful in a bowl of coffee (she likes her coffee chicory-flavored and strong). The rest we divide between a pair of jelly glasses. We're both quite awed at the prospect of drinking straight whiskey; the taste of it brings screwed-up expressions and sour shudders. But by and by we begin to sing, the two of us singing different songs simultaneously. I don't know the words to mine, just: *Come on along, come on along, to the dark-town strutters' ball.* But I can dance: that's what I mean to be, a tap dancer in the movies. My dancing shadow rollicks on the walls; our voices rock the chinaware; we giggle: as if unseen hands were tickling us. Queenie rolls on her back, her paws plow the air, something like a grin stretches her black lips. Inside myself, I feel warm and sparky as those crumbling logs, carefree as the wind in the chimney. My friend waltzes round the stove, the hem of her poor calico skirt pinched between her fingers as though it were a party dress: *Show me the way to go home,* she sings, her tennis shoes squeaking on the floor. *Show me the way to go home.*

Enter: two relatives. Very angry. Potent with eyes that scold, tongues that scald. Listen to what they have to say, the words tumbling together into a wrathful tune: "A child of seven! whiskey on his breath! are you out of your mind? feeding a child of seven! must be loony! road to ruination! remember Cousin Kate? Uncle Charlie? Uncle Charlie's brother-in-law? shame! scandal! humiliation! kneel, pray, beg the Lord!"

Queenie sneaks under the stove. My friend gazes at her shoes, her chin quivers, she lifts her skirt and blows her nose and runs to her room. Long after the town has gone to sleep and the house is silent except for the chimings of clocks and the sputter of fading fires, she is weeping into a pillow already as wet as a widow's handkerchief.

"Don't cry," I say, sitting at the bottom of her bed and shivering despite my flannel nightgown that smells of last winter's cough syrup, "don't cry," I beg, teasing her toes, tickling her feet, "you're too old for that."

"It's because," she hiccups, "I *am* too old. Old and funny."

"Not funny. Fun. More fun than anybody. Listen. If you don't stop crying you'll be so tired tomorrow we can't go cut a tree."

She straightens up. Queenie jumps on the bed (where

Queenie is not allowed) to lick her cheeks. "I know where we'll find pretty trees, Buddy. And holly, too. With berries big as your eyes. It's way off in the woods. Farther than we've ever been. Papa used to bring us Christmas trees from there: carry them on his shoulder. That's fifty years ago. Well, now: I can't wait for morning."

Morning. Frozen rime lusters the grass; the sun, round as an orange and orange as hot-weather moons, balances on the horizon, burnishes the silvered winter woods. A wild turkey calls. A renegade hog grunts in the undergrowth. Soon, by the edge of knee-deep, rapid-running water, we have to abandon the buggy. Queenie wades the stream first, paddles across barking complaints at the swiftness of the current, the pneumonia-making coldness of it. We follow, holding our shoes and equipment (a hatchet, a burlap sack) above our heads. A mile more: of chastising thorns, burs and briers that catch at our clothes; of rusty pine needles brilliant with gaudy fungus and molted feathers. Here, there, a flash, a flutter, an ecstasy of shrillings remind us that not all the birds have flown south. Always, the path unwinds through lemony sun pools and pitch vine tunnels. Another creek to cross: a disturbed armada of speckled trout froths the water round us, and frogs the size of plates practice belly flops; beaver workmen are building a dam. On the farther shore, Queenie shakes herself and trembles. My friend shivers, too: not with cold but enthusiasm. One of her hat's ragged roses sheds a petal as she lifts her head and inhales the pine-heavy air. "We're almost there; can you smell it, Buddy?" she says, as though we were approaching an ocean.

And, indeed, it is a kind of ocean. Scented acres of holiday trees, prickly leafed holly. Red berries shiny as Chinese bells: black crows swoop upon them screaming. Having stuffed our burlap sacks with enough greenery and crimson to garland a dozen windows, we set about choosing a tree. "It should be," muses my friend, "twice as tall as a boy. So a boy can't steal the star." The one we pick is twice as tall as me. A brave handsome brute that survives thirty hatchet strokes before it keels with a creaking rending cry. Lugging it like a kill, we commence the long trek out. Every few yards we abandon the struggle, sit down and pant. But we have the strength of triumphant huntsmen;

that and the tree's virile, icy perfume revive us, goad us on. Many compliments accompany our sunset return along the red clay road to town; but my friend is sly and noncommittal when passers-by praise the treasure perched on our buggy: what a fine tree and where did it come from? "Yonderways," she murmurs vaguely. Once a car stops and the rich mill owner's lazy wife leans out and whines: "Giveya two-bits cash for that ol tree." Ordinarily my friend is afraid of saying no; but on this occasion she promptly shakes her head: "We wouldn't take a dollar." The mill owner's wife persists. "A dollar, my foot! Fifty cents. That's my last offer. Goodness, woman, you can get another one." In answer, my friend gently reflects: "I doubt it. There's never two of anything."

Home: Queenie slumps by the fire and sleeps till tomorrow, snoring loud as a human.

A trunk in the attic contains: a shoebox of ermine tails (off the opera cape of a curious lady who once rented a room in the house), coils of frazzled tinsel gone gold with age, one silver star, a brief rope of dilapidated, undoubtedly dangerous candy-like light bulbs. Excellent decorations, as far as they go, which isn't far enough: my friend wants our tree to blaze "like a Baptist window," droop with weighty snows of ornament. But we can't afford the made-in-Japan splendors at the five-and-dime. So we do what we've always done: sit for days at the kitchen table with scissors and crayons and stacks of colored paper. I make sketches and my friend cuts them out: lots of cats, fish too (because they're easy to draw), some apples, some watermelons, a few winged angels devised from saved-up sheets of Hershey-bar tin foil. We use safety pins to attach these creations to the tree; as a final touch, we sprinkle the branches with shredded cotton (picked in August for this purpose). My friend, surveying the effect, clasps her hands together. "Now honest, Buddy. Doesn't it look good enough to eat?" Queenie tries to eat an angel.

After weaving and ribboning holly wreaths for all the front windows, our next project is the fashioning of family gifts. Tie-dye scarves for the ladies, for the men a home-brewed lemon and licorice and aspirin syrup to be taken "at the first Symptoms of a Cold and after Hunting." But when it comes time for making each other's gift, my friend and I separate to work secretly. I would like to buy her a pearl-handled knife, a radio, a whole pound of chocolate-covered cherries (we tasted some once, and she always swears: "I could live on them, Buddy, Lord yes I could—and that's not taking His name in vain"). Instead, I am building her a kite. She would like to give me a bicycle (she's said so on several million occasions: "If only I could, Buddy. It's bad enough in life to do without something *you* want; but confound it, what gets my goat is not being able to give somebody something you want *them* to have. Only one' of these days I will, Buddy. Locate you a bike. Don't ask how. Steal it, maybe"). Instead, I'm fairly certain that she is building me a kite—the same as last year, and the year before: the year before that we exchanged slingshots. All of which is fine by me. For we are champion kite-fliers who study the wind like sailors; my friend, more accomplished than I, can get a kite aloft when there isn't enough breeze to carry clouds.

Christmas Eve afternoon we scrape together a nickel and go to the butcher's to buy Queenie's traditional gift, a good gnawable beef bone. The bone, wrapped in funny paper, is placed high in the tree near the silver star. Queenie knows it's there. She squats at the foot of the tree staring up in a trance of greed: when bedtime arrives she refuses to budge. Her excitement is equaled by my own. I kick the covers and turn my pillow as though it were a scorching summer's night. Somewhere a rooster crows: falsely, for the sun is still on the other side of the world.

"Buddy, are you awake?" It is my friend, calling from her room, which is next to mine; and an instant later she is sitting on my bed holding a candle. "Well, I can't sleep a hoot," she declares. "My mind's jumping like a jack rabbit. Buddy, do you think Mrs. Roosevelt will serve our cake at dinner?" We huddle in the bed, and she squeezes my hand I-love-you. "Seems like your hand used to be so much smaller. I guess I hate to see you grow up. When you're grown up, will we still be friends?" I say always. "But I feel so bad, Buddy. I wanted so bad to give you a bike. I tried to sell my cameo Papa gave me. Buddy"—she hesitates, as though embarrassed—"I made you another kite." Then I confess that I made her one, too; and we laugh. The candle burns too short to hold. Out it goes, exposing the starlight, the stars spinning at the window like a visible caroling that slowly, slowly daybreak silences. Possibly we doze; but the beginnings of dawn splash us like cold water: we're up, wide-eyed and wandering while we wait for others to waken. Quite deliberately my friend drops a kettle on the kitchen floor. I tap-dance in front of closed doors. One by one the household emerges, looking as though they'd like to kill us both; but it's Christmas, so they can't. First, a gorgeous breakfast: just everything you can imagine—from flapjacks and fried squirrel to hominy grits and honey-in-the-comb. Which puts everyone in a good humor except my friend and I. Frankly, we're so impatient to get at the presents we can't eat a mouthful.

Well, I'm disappointed. Who wouldn't be? With socks, a Sunday school shirt, some handkerchiefs, a hand-me-down sweater and a year's subscription to a religious magazine for children. *The Little Shepherd*. It makes me boil. It really does.

My friend has a better haul. A sack of Satsumas, that's her best present. She is proudest, however, of a white wool shawl knitted by her married sister. But she *says* her favorite gift is the kite I built her. And it *is* very beautiful; though not as beautiful as the one she made me, which is blue and scattered with gold and green Good Conduct stars; moreover, my name is painted on it, "Buddy."

"Buddy, the wind is blowing."

The wind is blowing, and nothing will do till we've run to a pasture below the house where Queenie has scooted to bury her bone (and where, a winter hence, Queenie will be buried, too). There, plunging through the healthy waist-high grass, we unreel our kites, feel them twitching at the string like sky fish as they swim into the wind. Satisfied, sun-warmed, we sprawl in the grass and peel Satsumas and watch our kites cavort. Soon I forget the socks and hand-me-down sweater. I'm as happy as if we'd already won the fifty-thousand-dollar Grand Prize in that coffee-naming contest.

"My, how foolish I am!" my friend cries, suddenly alert,

like a woman remembering too late she has biscuits in the oven. "You know what I've always thought?" she asks in a tone of discovery, and not smiling at me but a point beyond. "I've always thought a body would have to be sick and dying before they saw the Lord. And I imagined that when He came it would be like looking at the Baptist window: pretty as colored glass with the sun pouring through, such a shine you don't know it's getting dark. And it's been a comfort: to think of that shine taking away all the spooky feeling. But I'll wager it never happens. I'll wager at the very end a body realizes the Lord has already shown Himself. That things as they are"—her hand circles in a gesture that gathers clouds and kites and grass and Queenie pawing earth over her bone—"just what they've always seen, was seeing Him. As for me, I could leave the world with today in my eyes."

This is our last Christmas together.

Life separates us. Those who Know Best decide that I belong in a military school. And so follows a miserable succession of bugle-blowing prisons, grim reveille-ridden summer camps. I have a new home too. But it doesn't count. Home is where my friend is, and there I never go.

And there she remains, puttering around the kitchen. Alone with Queenie. Then alone. ("Buddy dear," she writes in her wild hard-to-read script, "yesterday Jim Macy's horse kicked Queenie bad. Be thankful she didn't feel much. I wrapped her in a Fine Linen sheet and rode her in the buggy down to Simpson's pasture where she can be with all her Bones . . ."). For a few Novembers she continues to bake her fruitcakes single-handed; not as many, but some: and, of course, she always sends me "the best of the batch." Also, in every letter she encloses a dime wadded in toilet paper: "See a picture show and write me the story." But gradually in her letters she tends to confuse me with her other friend, the Buddy who died in the 1880's; more and more thirteenths are not the only days she stays in bed: a morning arrives in November, a leafless birdless coming of winter morning, when she cannot rouse herself to exclaim: "Oh my, it's fruitcake weather!"

And when that happens, I know it. A message saying so

merely confirms a piece of news some secret vein had already received, severing from me an irreplaceable part of myself, letting it loose like a kite on a broken string. That is why, walking across a school campus on this particular December morning, I keep searching the sky. As if I expected to see, rather like hearts, a lost pair of kites hurrying toward heaven.

A Christm

as Memory

the script

FADE IN:

The dark screen slowly begins to assume color: a pale, pastel washed-out blue. For several beats it is impossible for us to distinguish what it is we are looking at. Then, slowly, the image begins to resolve—a cloudless, pre-dawn sky which blends with a horizon line made indistinguishable because of the limpidity of the light and the softness of a whispy early morning ground fog. The sun is about to rise and as the light increases, we begin to distinguish the graceful shapes of the bare trees of a Southern winter landscape. We see that the grass is rimed with morning frost. The first sound now: a distant but clear tolling bell breaks the still, wintry air. The scene must be one of great beauty reflecting the pastoral and bucolic innocence of a time and place sweetly recalled.

On the horizon comes the first flame of the rising sun, its orange rind in powerful contrast to the blue-gray wash of the landscape. Music gently begins. The sun continues to violate the pellucid unity of ground and sky. Now, slowly, CAMERA PANS, losing the sun, to a large faded spreading old house. The architectural grace of the house is emphasized by the softness of light and perhaps even the softness of focus with which we might summon and visualize a precious memory of childhood.

CAMERA *begins a slow tracking shot toward the house. We are looking at what must be a kitchen wing. Healthy wood smoke streams from the chimney, while the light from the windows seems warm and inviting. As* CAMERA *moves closer, music continues and we hear:*

> NARRATOR
> (*softly, voice-over*)
> A coming of winter morning more than thirty years ago . . .

Now the CAMERA *has drawn in on the kitchen window, concentrating on a particular frosted pane which reflects the half-orb of the still rising sun. Through the frost and behind the window we see a Woman with almost white hair. Her face is remarkable —not unlike Lincoln's, craggy like that, and tinted by sun and wind; but it is delicate too, finely boned, and her eyes are sherry-colored and timid. Much of this we shall see in a moment, as the image of her face now is blurred by the scrim of the icy windowpane.*

CAMERA *draws tighter, concentrating on the reflected rising sun. When its orange nearly fills the screen, we* LAP DISSOLVE *through to an*

EXTREME CLOSEUP *of a roaring fire.*

> NARRATOR
> (VO)
> Just today the fireplace commenced its seasonal roar.

CAMERA *pulls back to reveal that we are inside the kitchen. Now we* PAN *to a* CLOSEUP *of the Woman whose face we half-saw from outside. Her eyes sparkle and her breath smokes the windowpane as she exclaims:*

> WOMAN
> Oh my! It's fruitcake weather!

CAMERA *begins a slow pullback from her face, gradually revealing a warm and enormous old-fashioned kitchen. It includes a great wood stove and a huge fireplace (both functioning in full fettle this early morning), a large wooden white-scrubbed round table and an atmosphere of faintly impecunious well-being. As CAMERA continues to pull back it reveals the seated back of a small boy happily involved in eating a large breakfast.*

> NARRATOR
> *(VO; starts speaking almost immediately after the Woman's line above)*
> The person to whom she is speaking is myself. I am seven: she is sixty-something. We are cousins, very distant ones, and we have lived together—well, as long as I can remember. Other people inhabit the house, relatives; and though they have power over us, and frequently make us cry, we are not, on the whole, too much aware of them. We are each other's best friend. She calls me Buddy, in memory of a boy who was formerly her best friend. The other Buddy died in the 1880's, when she was still a child. She is still a child.

During the foregoing, the CAMERA completes a thorough investigation of this warm, wonderful room and its two occupants, noting such details as the woman's tennis shoes and her shapeless gray sweater worn over a summery calico dress.

> WOMAN
> *(to the boy, excitedly)*
> It is! It's fruitcake weather! I knew it before I got out of bed. The Courthouse bell sounded so cold and clear. And there were no birds singing. They've gone to warmer country, yes indeed!

She sees Buddy is still happily packing his breakfast away. She crosses to him and snatches his plate.

> WOMAN
> Oh, Buddy, stop stuffing biscuit and fetch our buggy!

He runs after her, takes the last biscuit off the plate and puts it in his mouth. The Woman rushes about clearing the table and piling the dishes in the drainboard. Buddy helps her but, fast as he moves, it isn't fast enough for her. He has the sugar bowl and is opening the cupboard to put it away.

WOMAN

Leave it Buddy. We've got to go. We've thirty cakes to bake!

Buddy drops the sugar bowl on the counter and runs to the coat rack, hurriedly puts on his cap and coat. He takes his long raggedy woolen scarf. The Woman ties it around his neck, the ends hanging down his back.

WOMAN

Raggedy old thing. I've got to knit you a new one.

BUDDY
(anxiously)

Not for my Christmas present?

WOMAN

Would I give you a scarf for *Christmas*? Would I do a thing like that?

He grins and runs out leaving her still straightening the kitchen.

Buddy comes down the back porch steps and runs to the shed. He opens the door and an instant later comes out wheeling an old rickety wicker baby buggy. Its paint has long ago worn away and its wheels wobble like a drunkard's legs. The buggy is half filled with firewood. He takes it out and piles it against the shed and then pushes the buggy at a great rate to the back porch. The Woman is just coming down the steps. She is wearing an old hand-me-down ill fitting coat and carrying her gloves.

BUDDY

Your hat! You forgot your hat!

WOMAN

Oh goodness, my hat!

She rushes back into the house. She is in a hall. She opens a closet stuffed with the outer clothes of other members of the family, umbrellas, boots on the floor, etc., a clutter of hats, caps, gloves and scarves on a shelf. She rummages around and finally pulls her hat out from under them. It is a straw cartwheel garlanded with faded velvet roses, some of them hanging loosely by a thread. As she claps it on her head one of the roses falls off. She picks it up and holds it uncertainly. She is torn by her desire to hurry and yet the rose is precious to her. On the narrow hall table there is a vase of flowers beneath a dim mirror and perhaps some photographs of relatives. The Woman puts the rose carefully among the flowers in the vase, catches a glimpse of herself in the mirror, straightens the hat from its first crazy angle to another just as odd and hurries out.

Buddy is down on his hands and knees peering under the house and whistling. Whatever he is whistling at is not answering.

> WOMAN
> Buddy, Buddy, where are you?

> BUDDY
> Under here. Queenie won't come out . . .

> WOMAN
> (bending down and whistling)
> Come on, Queenie, come on, we're going to the pecan grove!

No movement from under the house.

> BUDDY
> You shouldn't have told her. She knows it's a long way.

> WOMAN
> (to the dog)
> Come on Queenie, I packed a big bone for your lunch!

Reluctantly a little orange and white rat terrier crawls out from under the house and the three of them set off. Buddy and the Woman walk as fast as they can, Queenie trails suspiciously behind them.

Here a series of lovely shots of their pilgrimage. The landscape and surrounding country remain a study in early morning pastel; in our horizon shots of the three we see the cloudless winter sky still the palest shade of blue. Over this montage we:

ROLL MAIN TITLES

Final shot of montage brings them to a new barbed-wire fence around the pecan grove, prominently featuring a sign "Callahan's Pecan Farm—Private Property—No Trespassing—Trespassers Will Be Prosecuted to the Fullest Extent of the Law."

EXTREME CLOSE-UP of the "No Trespassing" sign. REVERSE to the faces of the Woman and Buddy.

They are surveying the fence with dismay.

> WOMAN
> Buddy, we're going in there!

> BUDDY
> How?

The Woman steps forward and picks up the top strand of the fence. Buddy gives her a look.

> WOMAN
> Go on!

Buddy looks around. It is clear he is more reluctant about this than she is. Finally he stoops and goes in under the fence. He holds the wire strand for the Woman. She pushes the buggy through and then bends to go under herself. Her sweater catches on a barb. She stops to untangle it.

> WOMAN
> I simply do not admire a man who puts up a barbed wire fence.

> BUDDY
> I don't either.

Pushing the buggy, they walk on into the grove.

PECAN GROVE. She takes off her hat and starts filling it with the windfall pecans. She has to search them out with her feet and kick away dead leaves. We get the idea that they're not at all plentiful and the task will be a long one. Buddy catches on, snatches off his own cap and does the same. There is an air of both gaiety and urgency about them. They're enjoying this but not as much as they would if the fence and the sign hadn't been there.

When hat and cap are full they run to the buggy, and dump in the nuts. All this running back and forth excites Queenie and she gambols around, barking happily.

WOMAN
(*to the dog*)
And you didn't want to come! Why you'd have
missed all the fun!

*They go farther into the grove in their search. The sign is still
on Buddy's mind.*

BUDDY
What'll we do if Mr. Callahan comes out here?

WOMAN
(*serenely*)
We'll thank him for his windfall pecans.

BUDDY
We could promise him a cake!

WOMAN
No, no, no, no! Our cakes are not bribes. Our
cakes are Christmas presents for the people we like
and admire.

BUDDY
Look! There's lots here!

The Woman bends down to see.

WOMAN
Lots of big ones!
(*she fills her hat and rises with a small groan*)
My back hurts!

BUDDY
Mine doesn't.

WOMAN
I should hope not. You're too young.

BUDDY
When I'm old, you'll be *very* old!

WOMAN
Then you'll have to bake all the cakes yourself.

BUDDY
No!

WOMAN

And I'm not gonna do a lick of work. I'm just gonna sit in my rocker and watch!

BUDDY

You'll never be *that* old!

EXTREME CLOSE-UP, A PECAN NUT in the strong grip of a large nutcracker which is fastened to the edge of the kitchen table. A loud crunch as the shell splinters. CAMERA draws back to reveal the two of them cracking nuts in front of the fire. Queenie begs for a taste and is rewarded. Buddy sneaks a pecan for himself.

WOMAN
(*a smile*)

Buddy, we mustn't do that! If we start we'll never stop, and there's scarcely enough as it is . . . for thirty cakes.

BUDDY

Are we going to the store tomorrow?

WOMAN

Yes, indeed. Right after lunch. Soon as I finish my ironing.

BUDDY

That's the part I like best. *Buying* things!

As they shell the pecans it is turning dark outside. The dusk turns the window into a mirror. Their reflections mingle with the rising moon as they work in the firelight. The bowl is piled high.

NARRATOR
(*VO*)

The only thing we don't have to buy for our cakes is the pecans. All the rest, cherries and citron, ginger and vanilla, candied pineapple, raisins and lemons, flour and butter and eggs . . . all that we have to buy at the grocery store. This involves money.

DISSOLVE TO:

THE WOMAN'S ROOM. It contains a scrap-quilted iron bed painted pink, chest of drawers, chair, her other meager belongings.

*Buddy and the Woman come into the room and close the door.
The Woman turns on a lamp. Their movements are quiet and
secretive—it is clear they are about to do something important
and do not want to be interrupted by any busybodies in the
house.*

*They kneel beside the bed, lift a loose floor board and withdraw
their treasure . . . an ancient bead purse. They throw themselves
on the bed and spill out the contents of the purse: a few tightly
rolled dollar bills, but mostly a pile of coins—and most of them
are pennies. They separate the coins into piles of fifty cent
pieces, quarters, dimes, nickels, pennies and begin to count.*

*The narration begins at the opening of the above scene and
continues throughout the counting.*

> NARRATOR
> (VO)
> My friend and I love to spend money but the
> trouble is we have so very little. Sometimes persons
> in the house provide skinflint sums. A dime is
> considered very big money. I console myself with
> the thought that they aren't my parents. What we
> do have, we've earned ourselves from various
> activities: holding rummage sales, selling buckets
> of hand-picked blackberries, and home made jam
> and peach preserves. We also round up flowers for
> funerals and weddings. Once we won seventy-ninth
> prize, five dollars, in a national football contest. Not
> that we know a fool thing about football. It's just
> that we enter any contest we hear about.

> BUDDY
> When we go to the store tomorrow let's go straight
> to our post box.

> WOMAN
> If you're thinking about the coffee-naming contest,
> it's too soon to get a letter.

> BUDDY
> They said, "Winners will be announced before the
> first of the year." What if we win!
> (*his eyes shine*)
> *Fifty thousand dollars!*

WOMAN
(trying out their entry for the thousandth time)
A.M. Coffee! I would like a pound of A.M. Coffee,
please. It does sound delicious Buddy. I wonder if
we ought to have added that slogan though. A.M.
Amen. People might think it's sacrilegious.

BUDDY
Coffee companies love slogans . . .
(confidently)
We're going to win first prize.

*By this time Buddy has counted the pennies and is on the
nickels. He is about to start the dimes. The Woman has been
counting the bigger coins. Before Buddy starts the dimes, she
takes four out of the pile and puts them in a separate place on
the bed.*

WOMAN
That's your picture show money until Christmas.

BUDDY
We'll need it for the cakes. I won't go to the picture
show.

WOMAN
I want you to go! I like to have you come home and
tell me the story.

BUDDY
Why don't you ever come with me?

WOMAN
I like to hear you tell me the story. Besides, a person
my age shouldn't squander their eyes. When the
Lord comes, let me see Him clear.

They continue the counting.

NARRATOR
(VO)
In addition to never having seen a movie, she has
never eaten in a restaurant, traveled more than five
miles from home, received or sent a telegram, read
anything except funny papers and the Bible, worn
cosmetics, cursed, wished someone harm, told a lie
on purpose, let a hungry dog go hungry.

They have stacked the money in neat piles according to denomi-
nation, and each of them has made his own count. They look
at each other in hopes their counts will agree.

> WOMAN
> (her voice a question)
> Twelve dollars and seventy-three cents?

> BUDDY
> I make it exactly thirteen dollars.

> WOMAN
> I hope not, Buddy! We can't mess around with
> thirteen. The cakes will fall. We'll put somebódy
> in the cemetery. Why, I wouldn't even get out of
> bed on the thirteenth.

> BUDDY
> Shall we count it over again?

> WOMAN
> (shakes head)
> Just to be safe, let's throw a penny out the window!

They are mightily impressed with the flamboyance of this notion. Judiciously, Buddy selects a single penny and hands it to
the Woman. She crosses to the window, opens it a crack and
flings the penny into the night.

DISSOLVE TO:

EXTERIOR. GENERAL STORE. The Woman and Buddy
pushing their baby carriage have come to town. They cross the
railroad tracks and head for the General Store which is pure
period 1935.

They wheel the buggy inside.

INTERIOR. GENERAL STORE. The store is jammed full of
all the wares and products needed by the people in the surrounding countryside—from molasses to rubber hip boots. As Buddy
looks around at all the wonders for sale his face is ecstatic. The
owner of the store is a neighborly man named Mr. Morrison.

> MR. MORRISON
> (to the Woman)
> Good afternoon, Ma'am. How are you all today?

WOMAN

Just fine thank you, Mr. Morrison. Now, I have a
long list and we are going to need your complete
attention.

MR. MORRISON

I shall indeed, Ma'am, give you my complete
attention.

WOMAN

We have thirty cakes to bake this year.

MR. MORRISON

That's a generous lot of cakes!

WOMAN

I recall that last year you didn't have enough of the
candied pineapple . . .

MR. MORRISON

We have plenty of it now . . . all the way from
Hawaii.

He opens a large jar and takes out a piece to show her.

WOMAN

I'll take a pound and a half.

MR. MORRISON
(*a warning*)

That's fifty cents a pound, Ma'am. Comes to
seventy-five cents!

*The Woman senses that he doesn't think she has the money.
Her chin goes up in the air. Her eyes turn icy. She hands the
bead purse to Buddy.*

WOMAN
(*loud and clear*)

Count it out, Buddy.
(*she consults her list*)

Now we want a large bottle of vanilla, five bottles
of little red cherries, two jars of citron, a box of ginger . . .

*We see that she has set Mr. Morrison hopping to get her sup-
plies. He's much too busy for more warnings or any doubts about
money.*

DESERTED TWISTING COUNTRY ROAD

Buddy and the Woman are pushing the buggy now loaded with grocery bags. Queenie is following them. The light has lessened. The raggedy moss hanging from the tree branches gives the atmosphere a faintly ominous cast.

> NARRATOR
> (VO)
> Of the ingredients that go into our fruitcakes, whiskey is the most expensive, as well as the hardest to obtain: State Law forbids its sale. But everybody knows you can buy a bottle from Mr. Haha Jones. And so we are bound for Mr. Haha's business address, a fish-fry and dancing café.

The three have approached Haha's café. We see a large log cabin festooned with chains of garish naked light bulbs. Their steps slow down. Even Queenie stops prancing and stays close by.

> NARRATOR
> (VO)
> People have been murdered in Haha's café. Cut to pieces. Hit on the head. There's a case coming up in court next month.

> WOMAN
> (*timidly*)
> Buddy.

> BUDDY
> What?

> WOMAN
> (*to whip up her own courage*)
> It isn't so bad looking, is it? It's real pretty—with all those decorations. I hope Mrs. Haha's home alone. Hope Mr. Haha isn't here.

> BUDDY
> Is he an Indian too?

> WOMAN
> (*nods*)
> They say he's gloomy. Never laughs. That's why they call him Haha.

The Woman and the Boy pause in front of the closed doorway of the shabby and apparently deserted café. Buddy steps reluctantly forward and knocks on the door. Queenie barks. No response. The two exchange frightened looks.

> WOMAN
> *(apprehensively)*
> Mrs. Haha, Ma'am? Anyone to home?

Slow footsteps from inside. Ponderously, the footsteps approach the door. Again, the old Woman and the boy exchange frightened looks. Queenie emits a low growl. Slowly the door opens; it is Mr. Haha Jones himself. He is a giant; he does have scars; he doesn't smile. He glowers down at his callers through Satan-tilted eyes and his low voice rumbles forth:

> HAHA
> What you want with Haha?

A long silence. Finally the Woman half-finds her voice, which whispers:

> WOMAN
> If you please, Mr. Haha, we would like a quart of
> your *finest* whiskey.

His eyes narrow even further. He frowns on them, prolonging the moment almost unbearably. Then slowly, a faint smile creases his weathered countenance as he booms:

> HAHA
> Which one of you is a drinking man?

> WOMAN
> Oh, we want it for making fruitcakes, Mr. Haha.
> Cooking.

> HAHA
> *(frowns again)*
> That's waste of good whiskey!

Nevertheless, he retreats into the shadowed café and seconds later appears carrying a bottle of daisy-yellow unlabeled liquor. He holds it to the light, demonstrating its sparkle.

> HAHA
> Two dollars.

She pays him, meticulously counting out each coin into his outstretched palm. Mr. Haha never takes his eyes off her face. When she is finished he jangles all the coins together and shakes them in his hand. His voice softens.

> HAHA
> Tell you what . . .
> *(he pours the coins back into the bead purse)*
> You just send me one of them fruitcakes instead.

> WOMAN
> *(startled)*
> You mean a sort of trade?
> *(he nods . . . she beams at him)*
> Thank you very much Mr. Haha, thank you very much indeed!
> *(she pokes Buddy)*

> BUDDY
> Thank you Mr. Haha.

Mr. Haha's face is fragmented by his unaccustomed broad smile as he looks at them both.

> WOMAN
> Evening to you Mr. Haha.

> BUDDY
> Evening, Mr. Haha.

Mr. Haha goes back into the café as they push the buggy back down the path.

> BUDDY
> *(overwhelmed)*
> Did you see that? He *smiled!*

> WOMAN
> Well he's a very lovely man. We'll put an extra cup of raisins in *his* cake!

The screen is filled with a bright incandescent flame color. MUSIC in strongly as CAMERA slowly pulls back to disclose that the center of our attention is the giant kitchen wood stove which is glowing like a lighted pumpkin. Now begins a MONTAGE of the furious activity of baking the cakes. The Boy and the Woman work silently, pleasurably, rapidly and with a smooth efficiency as eggbeaters whirl, spoons spin round in bowls of butter and sugar and the mixture takes shape. In this MONTAGE we cover all the major processes from the breaking of the first egg, through the baking of the first four cakes (the most the oven will hold), the triumphant removal from the oven, the delicate dampening with whiskey of the freshly baked cakes, etc.

Finally, proud and exhausted, they stand in the center of the kitchen surrounded by their achievements which bask on window sills and shelves.

Under the following, the cakes are boxed individually, wrapped for mailing in paper and string, addressed, taken to the Post Office, stamped (the last of their coins go for this), and committed lovingly to the care of the United States Postal Authorities.

    NARRATOR
    (VO)
Who are our cakes for? Friends. Not necessarily
neighbor friends: indeed, the larger share are
intended for persons we've met maybe once, perhaps
not at all. People who've struck our fancy. Like
President Roosevelt. Like the Reverend and Mrs. J. C.
Lucey, Baptist missionaries to Borneo who lectured
here last winter. Or the little knife grinder who comes
through town twice a year. Or Abner Packer, the
driver of the six o'clock bus from Mobile, who
exchanges waves with us every day as he passes in
a dust-cloud whoosh. Or the young Wistons, a
California couple whose car one afternoon broke
down outside the house and who spent a pleasant
hour chatting with us on the porch (young Mr.
Wiston snapped our picture, the only one we've ever
had taken). Is it because my friend is shy with
everyone *except* strangers that these strangers, and
merest acquaintances, seem to us our truest friends?

I think yes. Also, the scrapbooks we keep of thank-you's on White House stationery, time-to-time communications from California and Borneo, the knife grinder's penny post cards make us feel connected to eventful worlds beyond the kitchen with its view of a sky that stops.

It is dusk as the exhausted pair return from the Post Office to the house. Followed by Queenie, they enter the kitchen and take off their coats.

> BUDDY
> Now it's all up to the Post Office of the United States of America!

> WOMAN
> (*turns on lights*)
> We can trust them, Buddy—as long as President Roosevelt's in charge.

She is busy starting the fire, putting the coffee pot on. Buddy's face has fallen as he looks around the kitchen.

> WOMAN
> Right after New Year's Day we can start to look for our thank-you notes.
> (*she turns and sees Buddy's face*)
> What's the matter with you?

Depressed, he has plopped down in a chair at the table.

> BUDDY
> The kitchen looks so empty. Everything's gone.
> (*the bead bag is on the table. He opens it and turns it upside down*)
> We're broke.
> (*looks at her glumly*)
> It's all over, isn't it?

> WOMAN
> My goodness, that's no reason to feel sad.
> (*Buddy's forlorn expression worries her*)
> We should feel proud and happy! We should celebrate!

The Woman looks around. An idea strikes her. She crosses to the cupboard and takes out the bottle of whiskey. There are two inches of liquid left in its bottom. She gets out a pair of jelly glasses.

> WOMAN
> We *are* going to celebrate!

Buddy and Queenie watch her curiously. She divides the whiskey between the two glasses. She gives one to Buddy. The other is for herself. She holds her glass up. She seems exhilarated at her own daring.

> WOMAN
> Have you ever tasted straight whiskey, Buddy?

> BUDDY
> You know I haven't. Have you?

The Woman shakes her head. Her eyes are glistening as she looks at the glass. Buddy sniffs his.

> BUDDY
> What if we don't like it?

> WOMAN
> Uncle Charlie loved it and we're both his relatives.
> Tastes run in families. You know!
> (*Buddy is about to try a sip*)
> Wait! We have to have a toast. We have to drink
> in *honor* of somebody.

She indicates that they should touch glasses.

> BUDDY
> (*cheered up*)
> I drink in honor of us!

> WOMAN
> To us!

They taste the whiskey, grimacing after the first swallow. Queenie watches them.

> BUDDY
> It's kind of strong . . .

                    WOMAN
                    (*her hand low on her chest*)
Feels nice and warm down here though. Uncle
Charlie was always drinking it for his chest colds.

                    BUDDY
                    (*another sip*)
I like it.

                    WOMAN
                    (*another sip*)
It wouldn't be in a fruitcake recipe if it wasn't good
would it?

*The Woman sees Queenie wagging her tail. She gets up from
the table and gets Queenie's bowl. She pours some coffee in it.
She is about to add a little whiskey from her own glass but
changes her mind. Instead she adds some from Buddy's glass.
She puts the bowl on the floor. Queenie laps it up eagerly. They
laugh.*

                    BUDDY
                    (*happily*)
Whiskey makes me feel sparky inside.

                    WOMAN
                    (*another drink*)
Carefree as the wind in the chimney . . .

*The Woman rises and begins to waltz around the room, the
hem of her dress pinched between her fingers. She stops behind
Buddy's chair and puts her arms around him.*

                    WOMAN
Oh, Buddy . . . you hurt my heart a minute ago
when you said this kitchen was empty. You know,
when you come home from a picture show and tell
me the stories I see everybody you talk about right
in this kitchen. I just see them before my eyes.
Sometimes there's so many people in here, there's
hardly room for me. Remember that one you told
me . . . my favorite. About the gypsies!
                    (*she picks up a pan and bangs on it as if it's
                    a tambourine. Her words are beginning to slur,
                    her movements are slightly unsteady as she
                    whirls about*)

When they were all dancing, remember? Round
and around and you told me they had their
tambourines jingling . . . Oh, I can just see it
now . . . I love all those dances. And remember the
one that had the tap dancers? What was the name
of that picture show . . . where the boys and girls
clickety-clacked . . . the way you showed me . . .
come on, get up and do it for me now.

*She almost pulls him out of his chair. He begins to tap dance,
his arms flying out at odd angles, his face beaming, his feet
clickety-clacking on the kitchen floor.*

*She continues to dance about in time to her own rhythm on the
tambourine, uttering wild little gypsy shouts, or rather her version of them.*

> BUDDY
> (*whirling around and around*)
> I'm going to be a tap dancer when I grow up. A
> tap dancer in the movies!

*Queenie gets into the spirit of the thing, frisking and barking
and rolling over on her back. The rollicking shadows of the two
dancers leap on the walls, their voices get louder and louder,
they grin and laugh and try to outdo each other.*

*Just when the noise and the dancing are at their height, two rela-
tives burst into the kitchen—two middle-aged aunts in neat
dark dresses. Their faces are severe. When they see the whiskey
bottle on the table, their eyes flash furiously.*

*The moment they appeared the dancing and singing stopped.
Buddy and the Woman stand in the crazy attitudes they've been
caught in as if they'd turned to statues. Queenie sneaks under
the stove.*

*The first relative snatches the two glasses and empties them into
the sink. The following dialogue from both of them is addressed
only to the Woman. It tumbles out wrathfully, one speech on
top of another.*

> SECOND RELATIVE
> Are you out of your mind? Feeding a child *whiskey*?

                    FIRST RELATIVE
A *little boy* with whiskey on his breath! Shame on
you!

                    SECOND RELATIVE
You've started him on the road to ruination . . .
that's what you've done! A *child* like that! You must
be looney!

                    FIRST RELATIVE
You *are* looney! Don't you remember Uncle Charlie?
Don't you remember Cousin Kate?

                    SECOND RELATIVE
What about Uncle Charlie's brother-in-law?

                    FIRST RELATIVE
If anyone in town hears about this . . . what a
scandal! Get down on your knees and pray . . .

                    SECOND RELATIVE
Beg the Lord to forgive you!

*With one last outraged glare, they turn on their heels and
march out of the room.*

*CAMERA pulls in for a full close up of the boy's face. He sees
that the Woman's eyes are brimming with tears, her lips are
quivering. His face is solemn with his own anguish for her. She
reaches up and turns out the kitchen light.*

                                        DISSOLVE TO:

*EXTREME CLOSE UP, the flame of a candle being carried.
CAMERA pulls back to reveal that Buddy is tiptoeing down a
dark hall. It is late night quiet as he knocks tentatively at the
Woman's door. No response. As he slowly opens her door, we
hear the faint and muffled sound of her weeping.*

*Clad in his flannel nightgown, he crosses the room and sits on
the bed, placing the candle on the night table. She continues
to cry very softly.*

                    BUDDY
                    (*with extreme delicacy*)
          Don't cry.
                    (*a pause*)
          You're too old for that.

Her tear-stained face turns up to look at the anxious boy.

> WOMAN
> It's because I *am* too old. Old and funny.

> BUDDY
> Not funny. *Fun.* More fun than anybody.
> *(he strokes her shoulder comfortingly)*
> Listen, if you don't stop crying you'll be so tired we
> won't be able to get our tree tomorrow.

*The thought of the tree captures her attention. She forgets about
her hurt feelings.*

> WOMAN
> *(excited)*
> Oh Buddy! I know where we can find real pretty
> trees. Pinecones big as pineapples. It's way off in the
> woods. Farther than we've ever been. Papa used to
> bring us Christmas trees from there . . . carry them
> on his shoulder. That's fifty years ago. Well now . . .
> *(she brightens)*
> I can't wait for morning!

*CAMERA pulls in for the tightest possible two shot emphasiz-
ing both the Woman's and Buddy's happy anticipation.*

DISSOLVE TO:

WOODS

*Buddy and the Woman pushing the buggy through some under-
growth and muddy places. Queenie running along behind.*

> WOMAN
> *(sniffing as though they are approaching the
> sea)*
> We're almost there! Can you smell it Buddy?

CUT TO:

GROVE OF PINE TREES

*Indeed it is like a kind of sea . . . scented acres of holiday trees,
green and fragrant . . . a beautiful grove just below them.*

They hurry down the grassy hill towards it.

IN THE GROVE

*They run from tree to tree trying to find the perfect one. They
each have burlap sacks which they stuff with pinecones.*

Finally the Woman finds a full-branched beautiful tree. While Buddy watches she takes a hatchet from one of the burlap bags and begins to chop it down. The chips fly and slowly the tree gives way.

Finally it keels over, its green branches falling straight towards the camera.

Lugging it proudly like the prize it is, they begin the long trek out to the road.

ROAD

The tree is safely in the buggy. They are headed for home down the red clay road. A car stops and a well-dressed woman leans out.

> WELL-DRESSED WOMAN
> *(in a whiny voice)*
> Give you two bits cash for that ole tree.

> WOMAN
> We wouldn't take a dollar.

> WELL-DRESSED WOMAN
> *(shocked)*
> A dollar? Fifty cents. That's my last offer.
> *(the Woman shakes her head)*
> My goodness, you can get another one.

> WOMAN
> *(gently)*
> I doubt it. There's never two of anything.

Disgusted, the Well-Dressed Woman grinds her gear shift and speeds on.

The CAMERA pulls in for a tight two shot as the Woman and Buddy continue homeward.

DISSOLVE TO:

ATTIC

Among the old trunks and furniture and other storage of the household Buddy has cleared a secret place. He is constructing what looks like a beautifully elaborate kite.

> NARRATOR
> (VO)
> Our next project is the fashioning of family gifts.
> Of course the most important present for each of us
> is that which we give one another. I am building
> her a kite. I am fairly certain that she is building
> me a kite; the same as last year, and the year before;
> the year before that we exchanged slingshots. All of
> which is fine by me. For we are champion kite-fliers
> who study the wind like sailors; my friend, more
> accomplished than I, can get a kite aloft when there
> isn't enough breeze to carry clouds.
>
> DISSOLVE TO:

INTERIOR. GENERAL STORE

Mr. Morrison is wrapping up a large gnawable bone.

> NARRATOR
> (VO)
> Christmas Eve we scrape together a nickel to buy
> Queenie's traditional gift.
>
> DISSOLVE TO:

DINING ROOM

*Buddy and the Woman are dressed in bathrobes, ready for bed.
Buddy holds Queenie in his arms. The Christmas tree is decorated. The Woman is placing Queenie's bone high among the
branches. Queenie is staring up at it in a trance of greed.*

> NARRATOR
> Our work is finished. Now, the long wait till
> dawn . . .
>
> DISSOLVE TO:

BUDDY'S BEDROOM. NIGHT

*The door opens and the Woman enters. She is carrying a small
kerosene lamp.*

> WOMAN
> (a whisper)
> Buddy? Are you awake?
> (the boy nods. The Woman crosses to sit on
> his bed. She puts the lamp down on the night
> table)

I can't sleep a hoot. My mind is jumping like a
jack rabbit!
     (*the boy smiles and takes her hand*)
Buddy do you think Mrs. Roosevelt will serve our
cake for dinner?

     BUDDY
I hope so!

She squeezes his hand. Suddenly her brow wrinkles.

     WOMAN
Seems like your hand used to be much smaller!
I guess I hate to see you grow up.
     (*looks at him for a long time*)
When you are grown up will we still be friends?

     BUDDY
Always.

     WOMAN
I wanted so bad to give you a bike for Christmas.
I tried so hard to sell my cameo Papa gave me.
Buddy . . .
     (*hesitates as though embarrassed, finally it
     comes out*)
I made you another kite!

     BUDDY
I made you a kite too!

     WOMAN
You did?

*They burst into laughter. Their laughter grows, becomes uproari-
ous as we*

                    DISSOLVE TO:

BUDDY'S BEDROOM. DAWN.

*Buddy and the Woman are stretched out on his bed asleep. The
first palings of dawn are visible at the window. His eyes snap
open. Motionless, he is wide awake. As though on cue, her eyes
open too. Wordlessly, they arise. She helps Buddy into a bath-
robe.*

KITCHEN. DAWN.

They come into the kitchen, each one carrying a very fancily wrapped package, each package has the unmistakable outlines of a kite.

> **WOMAN**
> Let's leave ours in here, Buddy.

He nods. They each prop a present up against the other's chair. They go on into the dining room.

DINING ROOM. DAWN.

Small piles of gaily wrapped presents under the tree, but clearly it is a family tradition that no one opens presents until everyone is assembled. Not a sound from upstairs. The two friends' frustration and impatience are obvious.

The Woman crosses to the potbellied stove. She lifts the lid and lets it bang down with a frightfully loud metallic sound. They listen. Still no one is stirring. The Woman lifts the lid again and grinning at Buddy keeps banging and clattering it. Buddy starts to tap dance making as much of a racket as possible. Suddenly they hear a door slam upstairs. Smiling at each other they stop the noise.

> **NARRATOR**
> *(VO)*
> The household emerges . . .

A sleepy pair of aunts enters the dining room. Their expressions are furious.

> **NARRATOR**
> *(VO)*
> Of course they would like to kill us both, but it's Christmas so they can't.

> **FIRST AUNT**
> *(in a sour unChristmasy voice)*
> Join hands!

Buddy and the Woman join hands with the two aunts and, facing the Christmas tree, the four of them sing the carol "Hark

the Herald Angels Sing." We realize this is another family tradition. As the CAMERA travels over the four faces we understand how different Buddy and his friend are from the other two, how immersed in their special friendship, how apart they are from the other two grim women.

When the carol is over Buddy runs to get his presents. He picks up the entire pile and carries it to a spot on the floor near the stove.

The three women sit down at the dining room table to open their packages.

Buddy is soon surrounded by torn tissue paper as he quickly unwraps each package. We see his gifts during the following:

> NARRATOR
> (VO)
> Well, I'm disappointed. Who wouldn't be? With
> socks, a Sunday school shirt, some handkerchiefs, a
> hand-me-down sweater and a year's subscription to a
> religious magazine for children: *The Little Shepherd!*
> It makes me boil. It really does!

The Woman has opened her presents too. Among them we see some pot holders, and a white knitted shawl. With the shawl over her shoulders she rises and crosses the room.

> WOMAN
> (*a murmur*)
> I'll just go and give the fire a poke . . .

She goes into the kitchen. Buddy looks over his presents again with extreme disgust. The Woman comes out of the kitchen. She stoops down to speak to Buddy.

> WOMAN
> I think you'd better drink your milk in the kitchen.

> BUDDY
> Why?

> WOMAN
> (*significantly*)
> Because it's in the kitchen, that's why!

Buddy jumps up and the two of them sneak out to the kitchen.

KITCHEN

As Buddy enters he sees a surprise—a little Christmas tree, decorated with countless white angels and a shiny silver star on its tip. His eyes widen, his whole face lights up as he approaches it and stares.

> BUDDY
> When did you do that?

> WOMAN
> The other night . . . when you were sound asleep
> dreaming whatever it is little boys dream about!

Buddy continues to admire the tree. She is delighted with his reaction. They look at each other and laugh.

> WOMAN
> Come on, let's open our presents.

Each one sits in his chair and starts the unwrapping. They don't tear the tissue paper off any which way as they have done in the other room but carefully untie the ribbons and detach the paper from its pasted seals, watching each other all the while. They manage to get the wrappings off simultaneously (which is the point) and the kites are revealed at the same time.

> WOMAN
> Oh Buddy! Mine's just beautiful!

Buddy stares at his kite. It is blue and scattered with gold good conduct stars. His name is painted on it.

> BUDDY
> (*really impressed*)
> Not as beautiful as mine!

> WOMAN
> Oh how I wanted to give you a bicycle!

> BUDDY
> I wanted to give you a whole pound of chocolate
> covered cherries!

> WOMAN
> It's bad enough in life to do without something *you*
> want . . . what gets my goat is not being able to give
> somebody something you want *them* to have.

But I'd rather have a kite! Really, I would!

One of these days I'm going to locate you a bike.
Don't ask how. *Steal* it, maybe.
> (*the waving branches outside the window
> catch her eye*)
> (*excited*)

Buddy! The wind is blowing!

EXTERIOR. BUDDY'S HOUSE.

*They have dressed and put on sweaters. Now they run out of the
house carrying their kites. They race to the pasture.*

We follow them as they perform the actions appropriate to:

NARRATOR
The wind is blowing and nothing will do till we've
run to a pasture below the house where Queenie
has scooted to bury her bone (and where, a winter
hence, Queenie will be buried too). We unreel our
kites, feel them twitching at the string like sky fish
as they swim into the wind. Satisfied, sun-warmed
we sprawl in the grass and watch our kites cavort . . .

*It is a radiant Christmas day. The grass of the pasture is golden
against the dazzling blue of the sky. The Woman looks about
them, her eyes feasting on the wonders of God's work, on
Buddy's contented small boy's face, on the whole lovely world
stretching to the horizon.*

WOMAN
My, how foolish I am! You know what I've always
thought? I've always thought a body would have
to be sick and dying before they saw the Lord.
And I imagined that when He came it would be
like looking at a Baptist window: pretty as colored
glass with the sun pouring through . . . such a shine
you don't know it's getting dark. And it's been a
comfort to me to think of that shine—taking away
all the spooky feeling. But I'll wager it never
happens. I'll wager at the very end a body realizes

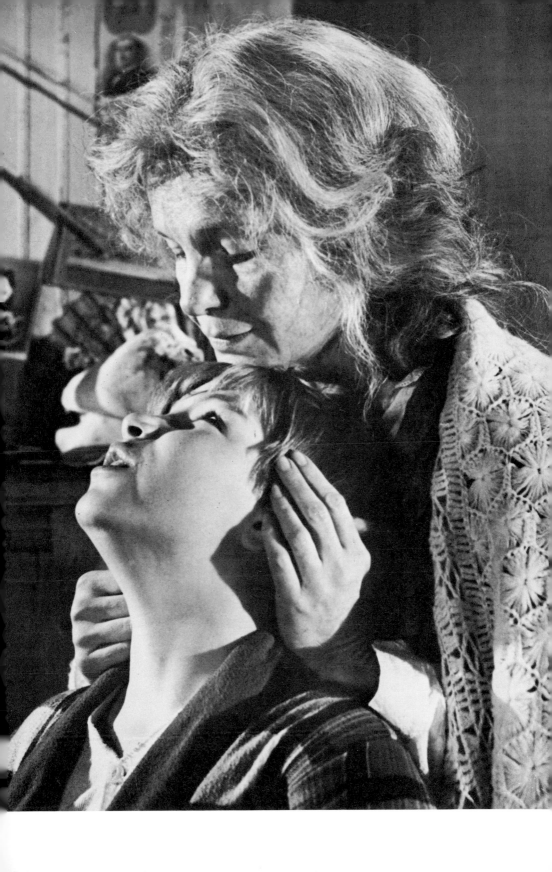

the Lord has already shown Himself. That things
as they are . . .
> (*her hand circles in a gesture that gathers*
> *clouds and kites and grass and Queenie pawing*
> *earth over her bone*)

. . . just what they've always seen, was seeing Him.
As for me, I could leave the world with today
in my eyes.

They continue to lie sprawled on the grass watching their kites
soaring high in the sky.

During the following the CAMERA leaves them and tilts up to
the horizon, it follows the uneven line of the horizon, past a
large tree and then tilts even further up to the sky where a single
small white cloud is floating.

> NARRATOR
> (VO)

This is our last Christmas together. Life separates
us. Those Who Know Best decide that I belong
in a military school. And so follows a miserable
succession of bugle-blowing prisons, grim reveille-
ridden summer camps. I have a new home too.
But it doesn't count. Home is where my friend is,
and there I never go. And there she remains,
puttering around the kitchen. Alone with Queenie.
Then alone.

> WOMAN
> (VO)

Buddy dear . . .

> NARRATOR
> (VO)

. . . She writes in her wild hard to read script . . .

> WOMAN
> (VO)

. . . yesterday Jim Macy's horse kicked Queenie
bad. Be thankful she didn't feel much. I wrapped
her in a fine linen sheet and rode her in the
buggy down to Simpson's pasture where she can
be with all her bones . . .

NARRATOR
(VO)
. . . For a few Novembers she continues to bake
her fruitcakes single-handed; not as many, but
some; and, of course, she always sends me . . .

WOMAN
(VO)
. . . the best of the batch . . .

NARRATOR
(VO)
. . . Also, in every letter she encloses a dime
wadded in toilet paper . . .

WOMAN
(VO)
. . . See a picture show and write me the story . . .

NARRATOR
(VO)
. . . But gradually in her letters she tends to confuse
me with her other friend, the Buddy who died in
the 1880's; more and more thirteenths are not the
only days she stays in bed: a morning arrives in
November, a leafless birdless coming of winter
morning, when she cannot rouse herself to
exclaim: . . .

WOMAN
(VO)
. . . Oh my, it's fruitcake weather!

CAMERA *slam cuts from the blue sky to the Boy's face. As the*
following narration continues underneath, CAMERA pulls in
for an EXTREME CLOSEUP of the Boy's eyes, then slowly
pans to his hand holding the kite string.

Then slowly, slowly, CAMERA begins a long pan up the kite
string till we find the two kites flying side by side in the wide
sky.

NARRATOR
(VO—Continuing)
. . . And when that happens, I know it. A message
saying so merely confirms a piece of news some

secret vein had already received, severing from me
an irreplaceable part of myself, letting it loose like
a kite on a broken string. That is why, on this
particular December morning, I keep searching the
sky. As if I expected to see, rather like hearts, a
lost pair of kites hurrying toward heaven.

*The two kites have indeed been released. They travel away from
us, becoming smaller and smaller until finally they merge as one
dot, one speck, in the infinite sky.*

END

film credits

WOMAN
Geraldine Page

BUDDY
Donnie Melvin

FIRST AUNT
Lavinia Cassels

SECOND AUNT
Christine Marler

STOREKEEPER
Win Forman

MR. HAHA JONES
Josep Elic

DIRECTOR/PRODUCER *Frank Perry*
SCREENPLAY *Truman Capote & Eleanor Perry*
MUSIC *Meyer Kupferman*
PHOTOGRAPHY *Vincent C. H. Sunby*
PRODUCTION DESIGNER *Gene Callahan*
FILM EDITOR *Ralph Rosenblum*
IN CHARGE OF PRODUCTION *Henry Spitz*
ASSISTANT TO MR. PERRY *Lynn Forman*
COSTUME DESIGNER *Anna Hill Johnstone*
RECORDING SUPERVISOR *Dick Vorisek*
ASSISTANT DIRECTOR *Dan Eriksen*
WARDROBE *Marilyn Putnam*
SCRIPT SUPERVISOR *Marguerite James*
CAMERA OPERATOR *Vincent Saizis*

A Christmas Memory was first televised by the American Broadcasting Company on December 21, 1966 and was rebroadcast December 19, 1967. It was honored with the Peabody Award as the best television program of the year. Additionally, it received first prize at the Monte Carlo International Television Festival, Best Program of the Year citation from the United States Television Critics Association, Emmy Awards for Geraldine Page, Truman Capote, Eleanor Perry and numerous other awards and prizes.

A Christm

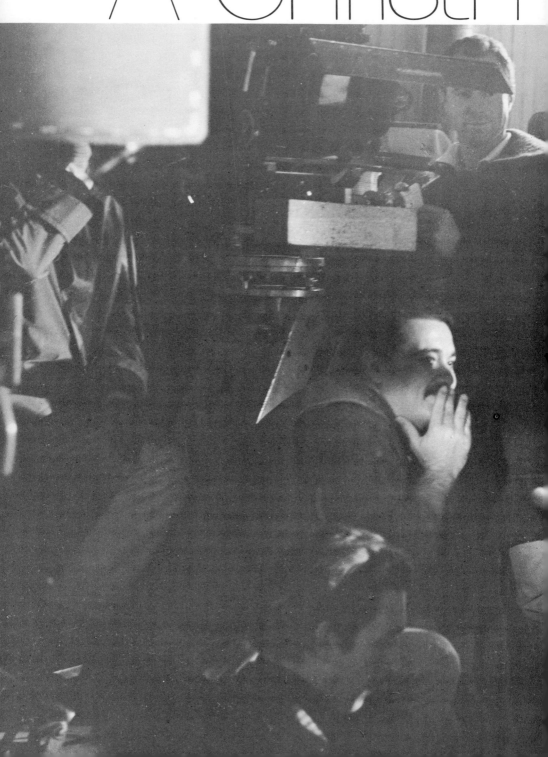

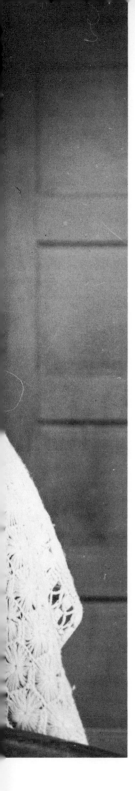

WHEN ONE IS DEALING with a mood piece as delicate
and lyrical as this story the most prudent thing
to do is to leave it alone—not even attempt to
adapt it to another medium. It is perfect as it is . . .
one runs too great a risk. This story survived for
two reasons: it was skillfully and sensitively
directed and acted and, of the three stories in
Trilogy, it was the least adapted.

the narrator

The use of narration was part of our effort to keep
the adaptation as close to the story as possible.
Ordinarily this device seems to be, in a way, a
crutch—an easy way out of having to dramatize or
"show" the content involved. However, in this
case it seemed totally appropriate since the
material is autobiographical and we would be
using the voice of the author himself.

the dramatization

As a comparison of the story and script will demonstrate, we either extrapolated scenes which already exist in the story or dramatized passages which were narrated. Two examples are the gathering of the windfall pecans and the whiskey drinking in the kitchen after the cakes have been mailed. The story is rich in suggestions for dialogue. For example, the lines on page 201 which tell about the coffee naming contest became the exchange in the script on pages 224 and 225.

The only scene we added which did not spring from something in the story is the brief one in the kitchen on Christmas morning. We used the surprise of the small tree as the motivation to get the two of them out of the parlor to unwrap their kites. Our only reason for this was to avoid having them play these intimate moments in front of the relatives.

The relatives appear for the first time during the whiskey-drinking scene. We felt their appearance was not only rather sudden but too late in the script. We would have preferred the audience to be aware of their presence in the house earlier but we couldn't find a scene for them that worked. The activities of Buddy and his cousin are so much between the two of them that any intrusion until the whiskey-drinking incident seemed artificial and awkward. We decided to settle for two allusions to the relatives in the narration: page 216 and page 224.

feature length

We wanted at one time to expand this story into a feature length film. To have done so would be in total contradiction to what I said earlier about not meddling with the story. Certainly we would have had a less personal film, less a mood-piece, less a memoir—but I still feel a full-length film based on this material would have worked on its own merits. Truman's Christmas memory is actually a beautiful love story between two unlikely human beings— outsiders who form a passionate alliance against the household and the world. This theme touches, it seems to me, a primary emotion in all of us— the yearning and the need for a loving, protective, adult figure. Almost everyone has experienced a separation (although not necessarily through death) from some such adored person. Both the happiness and the grief that come with such a relationship are universal enough to reach and involve an audience.

some ideas for expansion

Practically everything that the author tells us
Buddy and his cousin did together provide
springboards for additional episodes. The account
of the pair's desperate efforts to raise money is
rich with clues. Suppose we watch the two of them
scrounge around the town trying to collect the
items for their rummage sales—we see what items
they are given (outrageous? funny?), we get to
see what the community is like, what kind of
people the neighbors are, the town's reaction to
this unconventional pair. Perhaps we show the
actual holding of the sale and create some dramatic
or comedic conflict which will occur during it.
The Fun and Freak Museum would make a good
scene, especially the demise of the three-legged
biddy chicken. What about the slaughter of the
flies and the presentation of their corpses to the
"others" for payment? Whose funeral do they
arrange funeral flowers for? Do they go to the
funeral?

What about the knife grinder's visit? Or the lecture
at the church by the Baptist missionaries? Do
they show photographic slides of the heathens in
Borneo? There might be a scene in the visit of the
California couple whose car breaks down in front
of the house and who take the photograph of
Buddy and his cousin. We might explore the
Woman's efforts to sell her cameo to buy Buddy a
bike, or some kind of scene at Haha's café or show
Buddy coming home from the picture show and
telling the story.

There would be time in a feature, too, to develop the characters of the relatives and to present them as human beings, well meaning and well intentioned—even though they have no understanding of what goes on in the little world of the kitchen.

Probably there would be scenes at the military school. We could see Buddy's loneliness and unhappiness in the cold, strange atmosphere of the school. What if one day he opened a letter in front of the other boys and a dime wadded in toilet paper fell out?

Possibly one could dramatize the very moment when Buddy knows his cousin has died. Suppose he is in a classroom. While the class is being conducted Buddy turns and stares towards the window. Suddenly he rises from his seat and crosses to it. (It is frosted over like the kitchen window in the opening sequence.) Buddy opens it and looks out. We see that the tree branches are bare. We realize that no birds are singing. Buddy is unaware of the irate frown of the instructor, the amused looks of his classmates. A strange grieving expression is on his face. He looks up and sees the two tiny lost kites in the sky.

These are the merest surface ideas which come to mind and are meant only to indicate that there is plenty of content in the story upon which to base an expanded script. Once one set to work on the content the very important requirements of structure and style would undoubtedly suggest themselves.

Callahan property list

KITCHEN

CLEANING EQUIPMENT
Bissel sweeper
dust mop
wet mop and bucket
broom (yellow corn)
feather duster
rug beater (wire not wicker)
Octagon Soap
Gold Dust Twins Soap Powder
Old Dutch Cleanser
agate bucket kept under sink

FURNITURE AND APPLIANCES
Hoover cabinet with sifter
armoire to be painted (remove
    panels in doors and replace
    with screening)
small table under window on porch
    side
4 chairs (all can be mismatched)
1 rocker
1 small stool (low)
1 high stool
step ladder (wooden and worn)
cheap andirons and fire tools
black andirons and fire tools

ice box
gas water heater
hanging light over table with
    manufactured (tissue) shade
kerosene lamp in case lights go out
rag rug by fireplace
small mirror near sink

GLASSWARES
8 dozen Mason jars of various sizes
4 dozen jelly glasses
set of mix matched dishes and
    glasses
large bowl (ocher) filled with eggs
cracked soup bowl and chipped
    agate pan for food and
    water for Queenie (place
    both on paper under window
    by sink)
large pickle crock with piece of
    gauze over top

HOUSEWARES
Diamond box matches
salt box and shaker (large, glass)
spices and herbs in commercial
    cans and boxes (some in jars)
cannister set (possibly rather new)

HOUSEWARES *(Cont.)*

clear beer bottles for vinegar syrup
 and bleach with stoppers
 (cork)
wooden dish rack
wooden towel rack
soap dish over sink
tin for splash over sink
jelly jars, Dr. Pepper bottles,
 strawberry cartons, etc., on
 shelves under sink
painted biscuit tin
National Baking Company
 hinged-top tin
all kinds of food in boxes and cans
 (original labels or can be
 faked)
all ingredients for making cakes
wax paper to line pans
wire rack for cooling cakes
flour board for biscuit making
sewing basket on mantel
pan under ice box

LINENS

12 old towels (as many different
 kinds as possible)
line of dish rags and possibly small
 pieces of clothing drying
 over stove
oldish cloths for wrapping cakes to
 keep them moist
apron on hook on door
oil cloth on table

POTS AND PANS

cake pans (if all types and sizes be
 sure to have tube pans)
ice cream mixer
pie pans
cornbread makers in wrought iron
 (sticks)
black iron skillets
iron dutch oven
iron griddle
tin oven for top of stove

UTENSILS

pecan cracker (see sketch) *most
 important*

wooden and agate spoons
old silver spoon worn flat on end
 (for mixing cakes)
silver in drawers along with all
 usual utensils (all very old
 and worn)

MISCELLANEOUS

stack of newspapers (by side of
 stove in box)
box for Queenie (other side of
 stove)
pressed tin for back of stove
linoleum on floor under stove
4 bricks (one under each leg of
 stove to lift)
2 fruit crates lined with old
 newspapers (used for
 vegetable storage)
candle in saucer
4 cigar boxes (to collect things in)
wood box by fireplace for twigs
 and chips of wood stacked
 next to it
blue ribbon
calendars, Christmas cards and post
 cards on mantel
worn afghan on rocker
scissors, paper, paste, stars, string
 and sticks, and kite tails and
 extra material to tear
flat, well-worn pillow on seat of
 rocker
pumpkin on floor by clothes rack
Chinese wind harp (if too trite,
 something like it)
bag hanging by door to pantry by
 string (another bag for
 clothespins)

PORCH

2nd ice box
empty bushel baskets
old trunk
porch rockers
bench against section end of stair
 with dead potted plants and
 old crocks
3 or 4 potting flats with small pots
wood stacked on porch in box

clothes line on porch or in yard
should there be evidence of
Christmas dinner supplies
when they open their
presents

BACK ENTRANCE TO KITCHEN

clothes hooks
mirror
table
vase flowers
old gun
fishing poles (bamboo)
dip net
crabbing nets
pruning shears
old calendar
2 folding yard chairs (wood or
canvas)

DINING ROOM

old Christmas decorations
wrapped presents
window shades
curtains
table and 10 chairs
armless sofa
table set for Christmas dinner
pictures
rug
2 pedestals in windows with plants
wax fruit on sideboard with
terrible fake poinsettias
around red candles
chandelier
scarves for buffet
lace cloth for table with
undercloth
plate rail with terrible dishes on
display
china closet with more of same

LIVING ROOM

drapes, lace and shades
secretary
2 side chairs
1 sofa

1 table with electric lamp
scarf for tables
2 plant stands in windows
Bible on table back of sofa
rug
chandelier

HALLWAY

console table and chair with
picture and vase
hall runner
wall sconce
possible old wheel chair for aged
member of family

GERRY'S BEDROOM

iron bed (thin not pipe)
lumpy mattress
sheets
thin blanket
patchwork quilt
bed table with thickly crocheted
scarf
small art glass lamp
bare bulb hanging from ceiling
painted chest of drawers
small trunk
Mother's picture
small dreadful picture
thin net half curtains
worn window shade
armless rocker
old rag rug by bed
bed pot under bed
old useless things saved by Friend
in truck (old candy box, hat
pins on card, old ruffled
blouse, Buddy's baby shoes,
handiwork that could
possibly have been for trous-
seau, trimmings)
pictures cut from magazines tacked
to wall back of bed (possibly
"Christ as the Little
Shepherd")

HOUSE EXTERIOR

well-worn wash tub hanging on
side of porch

HOUSE EXTERIOR (*Cont.*)

large iron sugar boiler on bricks
    near porch
laundry line with pin bag hanging
    from it (no clothes)
bird house on pole made to look
    like house
very crude chicken coop with
    chickens
abandoned dog house

UNDER HOUSE

rusty lawn mower
broken pickle crock
strawberry flats and an orange crate
    or two
twisted roll of fence wire
empty terra cotta flower pots in all
    sizes for potting
trim some vines over porch
matching curtains and window
    shades from kitchen interior
faded Red Cross sticker on window
possibly old shrubbery and the
    hind of old flower beds on
    back fence
when they leave on shopping tour
    or whatever have model T
    and a wagon passing one
    another on road and if we
    can manage it, a hound dog
    in one of them.

ATTIC

dress form
old sewing machine

curtain stretcher (this could be
    used with curtain on it in
    the yard)
dried flowers hanging from rafters
old trunks and luggage generally
boxes and boxes
empty picture frames
broken chair hung from rafter
rolls of grass matting (Japanese)
old shutters
tin bathtub
stacks of magazines tied up with
    string
folders of old canceled checks and
    ledgers from old family
    business
stacks of newspapers
school desk
old hand clothes washer
old rugs (folded)
row of old kerosene lamps now
    retired
some lumber laid over floor rafters
laundry bags of old scraps etc.
old mattresses
croquet set
old easel for framed picture
chamber pots and wash bowls
bundles of shingles for replacement
if possible make a tent of old
    blankets that Buddy might
    have used as a hideaway
    with table made from box
    with candle on it and child's
    book etc. (might have made
    kite there)